ghIlghameS

ghIlghameS

A Klingon Translation

Translated by
Roger Cheesbro

Introduction by
Lawrence M. Schoen

Cover Art by
David Schaefer

Layout and Design by
Lawrence M. Schoen

qo'mey poSmoH Hol

language opens worlds

Introduction

Recently, a joint Imperial-Federation research team operating along the Neutral Zone made an astounding discovery. They stumbled upon a lone Klingon scout ship, or rather, its remains. An impressive impact crater revealed the vessel had crashed upon a tiny planetoid in the midst of an uncharted asteroid field located on the edge of Imperial space. The sole occupant survived the crash, but powerful magnetic fluctuations in the area blocked any distress signal that might have been sent. Eventually, the survivor appears to have dismantled his ship, and erected eleven duranium bulkheads upon an otherwise barren plain. We know nothing more of this individual, not his name, nor his house, nor his family line. Years (perhaps centuries?) of exposure to space, radiation, and an endless barrage of particulate matter, have swept away almost all evidence of his presence. Only the duranium slabs remain. They are his sole legacy, a tale he left behind upon these metal plates, incised in row after row of precise pIqaD, the Klingon writing system.

Holograms of each slab were transmitted to the Institute of Knowing on Kronos, the fabled Vulcan Science Academy, and to Starfleet Academy on Earth. Both the Klingon and Vulcan linguistic teams found only a riveting narrative adventure, presumably the basis for a new opera by an unknown composer. The Terran researchers, however, realized it to be much more. The marooned Klingon, far from home and with no hope of rescue, had translated and transcribed the epic of Gilgamesh.

Why this work, alien and bizarre, and not some other? Why not leave behind a traditional Klingon story or an opera's libretto, or a fable of the legendary Kahless? No explanation is provided, only the text itself. All the rest is speculation. We can ask what appeal this Terran tale might have for a desolate Klingon. What could be so compelling to drive him to such effort? How would a warrior — from an empire of warriors — react to the repeated fear of death which is a major theme of the epic? Would a Klingon find within the civilized Gilgamesh and the savage Enkidu the two halves of Klingon nature? And what of the capriciousness of the gods themselves, are they very different, these ancient Terran deities, from their own gods which the Klingons themselves slew in their own distant past? Dozens of compelling motivations have been voiced in the short time since this discovery, and they seem destined to remain simple conjecture, part of the larger riddle of the Klingon psyche.

It is unlikely that the mystery of precisely when or how a Klingon even acquired the epic of Gilgamesh will ever be known. The fierce magnetic storms which daily bombard the Gilgamesh planetoid (as it has come to be known) make it impossible to date the age of the surviving duranium plates. The utilitarian nature of Klingon design has produced only minimal changes in many aspects of ship construction and bulkheads of this sort are virtually indistinguishable, even in their pristine state. One positive note: Federation scholars have expressed relief that the Klingon Empire has made no attempt to claim this story as their own, avoiding the creation of a new controversy similar to the still raging debate surrounding Shakespeare's writings.

Already some critics have speculated that the Klingon scribe never actually visited Earth, but instead received the epic from a third party. The transliteration of some terms (e.g., **SIyDIr** for "cedar") and the complete absence from the translation of specific flora and fauna (e.g., "scorpions" in Tablet IX) have been presented as evidence of this interpretation. However, such arguments are quickly countered by the use and adaptation of Klingon terms to describe yet other instances (e.g., **vIghro''a'** for "lion."). To further complicate the situation, retranslation of the Klingon version suggests that the source for this particular telling of the epic is neither the various manuscripts currently known to originate in Nineveh or the Assyrian cities of Ashur, Kalah, or Huzirina, nor the version found in Babylon and Uruk. Whether this is a function of the Klingon scribe's idiolect, damage done to the duranium bulkheads, or lapses or variation in the tale as he received it (whether from a third party or directly) remains unknown and possibly unknowable.

And yet, the eleven bulkheads themselves bear more subtle tales, specifically about the unknown Klingon who incised them. Enkidu's initial fear before confronting Humbaba while true to the ancient text is virtually unheard of in any period of Klingon culture. This leaves modern day scholars to wonder if the Klingon scribe was simply being true to the translation despite the innate vulgarity of it (from a Klingon perspective) or, alternately, in his hopeless situation did he merely voice a trepidation that has existed in many a warrior's heart? Even this view is clearly taboo, but somewhat more palatable given the final outcome, lending a sense of redemption to Enkidu's ultimate behavior. There are gaps in this section of the tale and even a Klingon who had mastered Akkadian must surely have been at a loss. How to make sense, even Human sense, of the weakness of Enkidu at this critical moment, and then justify his recovery? This is no minor *faux pas* which can be brushed aside with a Klingon replacement proverb. Enkidu has dishonored himself, and Gilgamesh cannot look the other way. Indeed, he battles his brother in a very Klingon manner at the first hint of Enkidu's fear.

The text that might explain Enkidu's restoration of honor and bravery remains missing from the original tablets to this day, and the Klingon translation — desperate to make some sense of things — fills the gap with several classic Klingon aphorisms — **nIteb Qob qaD jup 'e' chaw'be' SuvwI'** *A warrior does not allow a friend to face danger alone* and **bIHeghvIpchugh bIHeghpu'** *If you are afraid to die, you are already dead*. This seems like precisely the advice Gilgamesh might have offered up and the result is quite satisfying in both languages.

Not surprisingly, since the discovery of the Gilgamesh planetoid the epic has caught the Klingon imagination. Everywhere in the Empire they understand and respond to this warrior. When Gilgamesh defeats Humbaba and desecrates the cedar grove, despite full knowledge of its value to the gods, the actions resonate with the untamable Klingon spirit. The Klingon epigram "Great deeds! Great songs!" seems to have been written for Gilgamesh. Operatic versions of the epic have already been mounted on the Klingon homeworld, and similar productions have spread throughout the Empire. On Morska, an eleven day festival, **ghIlghameS yupma'**, features staged performances, complete with costumes and props that evoke Klingon history but have no resemblance to Sumerian dress of that time. Even more unusual is a very controversial play on Vaq'aj II, a relatively recently conquered world of the Empire. The play consists of a dialog between Gilgamesh and Kahless and explores the future role of the Klingon people in the modern galaxy.

Ironically, the discovery of the Gilgamesh planetoid has resulted in thousands of Federation scholars adding one or more dialects of Klingon to their linguistic resumes alongside Akkadian and Sumerian. Their hope, however faint, is to glean some new insight from an outsider's translation, and perhaps to at last unravel mysteries (e.g., the "stone things" from Tablet X) that have left them puzzled up to now. As an aid to this, an English translation of the Klingon version has been provided on facing pages. Students new to the Klingon language will find this particularly helpful. As a further aid, a brief appendix of has been provided to aid in puzzling out the transliteration of proper names throughout the text.

Although this version of Gilgamesh — like all versions before it — is incomplete, absent fragments have not been marked as such. Instead, the story itself has been allowed to continue through.

Doubtless there are places in the text where an alternate term might be supplied, but the translation provided by Cheesbro (or **DloraH**, as he is called among Klingon scholars) is considered the best possible attempt at this time. The Klingon preference for terse utterances is well suited to the Akkadian poetic line, and virtually all of the Klingon sentences consist of a single line. Like most Klingon epics, this tale is meant to be read aloud, preferably to a gathering. This intent is reflected in the holograms from the original bulkheads, from which this edition was prepared. Grammatical license has been taken for this reason, paralleling the more relaxed style of discourse typically found when Klingons come together to share a tale. Certainly a similar consideration is the rightful due of this oldest of Earth's epics.

Lawrence M. Schoen, Ph.D.
KLI Director

ghIlghameS

nagh beQ wa'

Hoch leghbogh ghaH, vIllH
Hoch ta'pu'bogh ghaH De' vI'ang
Hoch Sovchu' ghaH   'e' chaw' 'anu
pegh legh ghaH
leghbe'lu'wI' tu' ghaH
qaSpa' SoD'a' qaSbogh wanI' ngoD qem ghaH

leng nI' SIQ, HoSDaj Hoch natlh
'ach roj 'e' ta'
nagh beQDaq Hoch ta'Daj qon
'uruq yergho chenmoH
'Iy'anna chIrgh reD chenmoH
bochbogh chIrgh reD tIlegh, baS rur
tlhoy' tInuD, rurlaH pagh
nagh yI'uch, tIQ!
'Iy'anna chIrgh, Daq'e' Dabbogh 'IStar, yIchol
pagh qach nIv law' qachvam nIv puS
'uruq yergho yIghoS 'ej yIyIt
yergho bIng yInuD, yergho naQ yInuDchu'
naghvam nIv law' latlh nagh nIv puS, qar'a'?
qach qech lucher Soch valchu'wI', qar'a'?
Soch qell'qam 'IStar chIrgh Daq Huv je,
qat 'uruq yergho

ngaSwI' yISam
yIngaQHa'moH
yIpoSmoH
tetlh yIlel 'ej yIlaD
ghIlghameS lut qonlu'

'uruqDaq bogh
Sub ghaH, nanbogh targh naS,
'etDaq yIt, DevwI',
ghotpu' QanwI',

Tablet I

He which has seen all, I introduce.

I reveal him that has accomplished everything.

Anu allowed him to be all-knowing.

He saw the secret.

He discovered that which was unseen.

He brought knowledge about events
that occurred before the Flood.

He endured a long journey, exhausted all of his strength;
but he accomplished peace.

He recorded all his accomplishments on stone tablets.

He built the walls of Uruk.

He built the Eanna Temple walls.

Look at the temple walls, which are shiny like metal.

Inspect the inner wall. None can compare.

Hold the rock. It is ancient!

Come close to the Eanna Temple, the dwelling of Ishtar.

No structure is more superior than this.

Go to the wall of Uruk and walk.

Inspect under the wall. Fully inspect the entire wall.

Is not this rock more superior than any other?

Did not the Seven Sages themselves design this structure?

Three leagues and the open courts of the Temple of Ishtar,
are contained within the walls of Uruk.

Find the container.

Unlock it.

Open it.

Take out the scroll and read it.

The stories of Gilgamesh are written.

He was born of Uruk.

He, a goring wild boar, was a hero;

a leader, he walked in front;

protector of people;

nagh reD Qaw'laHbogh SoD naS'e'!
HoSchu' ghIlghameS, lughalbanDa puqloD
Dunchu' ghIlghameS, nInSun puq
HuDmey poSmoH ghaH
bIQ'a'Daq leng ghaH
'utanapIStIm, HopwI', Sam ghaH
vengmey'e' Qaw'bogh SoD'a' chenqa'moH ghaH
ghaH nIv law' Hoch voDleH nIv puS
rurlaH 'Iv?
maqlaHchu' ghIlghameS neH,
jatlh,
<voDleH jIH!>
wejmaH wej vatlhvI' Human, javmaH jav vatlhvI' Qun
porghDaj qech cher Qun Dun, 'aruru
chenmoH
'IH
ghaH 'IH law' Hoch loD 'IH puS
pup
jen nachDaj, Hem, HoS
ghaHDaq nuH peplaH pagh ghol
'uruq DunmoH ghaH
veng Dun

'ach jach nuvpu'Daj,
jatlh,
<qu'qu' ghaH, nuQIH>

bep nuvpu' 'e' Qoy Qunpu'
vaj 'uruq joH'a', 'anu, lutlhob Qunpu',
jatlh,
<loD HoSghaj DachenmoHba'
ghaHDaq nuH peplaH pagh ghol
HoS
qu'
'ej nuvpu' QIH>

a fierce flood that is able to destroy stone walls!

Gilgamesh, son of Lugalbanda, was truly strong.

Gilgamesh, offspring of Ninsun, was most wonderful.

He opened the mountains.

He traveled the seas.

He found Utanapishtim, the Faraway.

He rebuilt the cities that were destroyed by the Great Flood.

Of all the kings, he was most superior.

Who can compare?

Only Gilgamesh can truly proclaim,

saying,

"I am king!"

One-third human, two-thirds god.

His body was designed by the great goddess Aruru.

She created him.

He was beautiful.

He was the most handsome man.

He was perfect.

His head raised, proud, strong.

No opponent could raise a weapon to him.

He made Uruk great.

A wonderful city.

But his people cried out,

saying,

"He is very fierce, he wrongs us."

The gods heard the people complain.

Thus the gods pleaded with Anu, the Lord of Uruk,

saying,

"You obviously created a powerful man.

No opponent can raise a weapon to him.

He is strong.

He is fierce.

And he wrongs the people."

'aruruvaD jach,

jatlh,

<loDvam DachenmoHta' SoH

DaH ghaHvaD yIjang

latlh yIchenmoH

tIqDaj qu' rurjaj ghaH

rojjaj 'uruq!>

QoyDI' 'aruru, ghopDu'Daj Say'moH,

lam puS tlhap

'ej HatlhDaq lan

HatlhDaq 'enqIyDu chenmoH

HoSghajqu'

law' pobDaj, Ha'DIbaH rur

tIq jIbDaj, be' rur

latlh ghot Sovbe', tayqeq Sovbe'

Ha'DIbaH tlhej, tIr tlhol Sop, bIQ tlhutlh

bIQmo' 'ojbe', Ha'DIbaH rur

bIQ DaqDaq 'enqIyDu qIH vonwI'

chaH jojDaq 'oHtaH bIQ Daq'e'

jaj wa'DIch, jaj cha'DIch, jaj wejDIch

bIQ DaqDaq ghom, chaH jojDaq 'oHtaH bIQ Daq'e'

'enqIyDu par vonwI'

vavDajvaD jatlh vonwI',

<vav, HuDvo' ghoS loD

ghaH HoS law' Hoch HoS puS

HoS, 'anu chunDab rur

bIQ DaqDaq Ha'DIbaHmey tlhej

bIQ Daq latlh DopDaq vIlegh

jIcholvIp

Dochmey vIchenmoHbogh Qaw' ghaH

Ha'DIbaH vIvonbogh tlhabmoH

jIvon 'e' bot ghaH>

They called out to Aruru.

They said,

"You created this man.

Now answer to him.

Create another.

May he be like his fierce heart.

May Uruk find peace!"

When Aruru heard this, she washed her hands,

she took a handful of dirt,

and placed it in the wilderness.

She created Enkidu in the wilderness.

He was very powerful.

He had much hair on his body, like an animal.

His hair was long, like a woman.

He did not know other people. He did not know civilization.

He accompanied the animals, ate the grass, drank water.

Like the animals, water quenched his thirst.

At the watering hole a trapper met Enkidu.

Each on opposite sides of the watering hole.

First day, second day, third day,

they met at the watering hole, the water between them.

The trapper did not like Enkidu.

The trapper spoke to his father,

"Father, a man came from the mountain.

Stronger than all.

He is strong, like the meteor of Anu.

He accompanies the animals at the watering hole.

I saw him on the other side of the watering hole.

I was afraid to get closer.

He destroys the things which I make.

He sets free the animals which I have trapped.

He prevents me from trapping."

jatlh vonwI' vav,

<puqloDwI', 'uruq Dab ghIlghameS

pagh HoS law' ghaH HoS puS

HoS, 'anu chunDab rur

'uruq yIghoS

ghIlghameSvaD loDvam yIDel

SoHvaD Sam'at, parmaq be', nob

yIqem

loDvam charghbej be'
bIQ DaqDaq tlhutlhtaHvIS Ha'DIbaH,
mopDaj teq be' 'ej 'ang'egh be',
yIra'

be' leghDI' loDvam, be'Daq chol

novchoH Ha'DIbaHDaj>

vavDaj qeS lob

'uruq ghoS vonwI'

paw 'ej 'uruq qoDDaq Qam

ghIlghameSvaD ghu' QIj,

jatlh,

<HuDvo' ghoS loD

ghaH HoS law' Hoch HoS puS

HoS, 'anu chunDab rur

bIQ DaqDaq Ha'DIbaHmey tlhej

bIQ Daq latlh DopDaq vIlegh

jIcholvIp

Dochmey vIchenmoHbogh Qaw' ghaH

Ha'DIbaH vIvonbogh tlhabmoH

jIvon 'e' bot ghaH>

vonwI'vaD jatlh ghIlghameS,

<yIjaH vonwI'

parmaq be', Sam'at, yItlhap

bIQ DaqDaq tlhutlhtaHvIS Ha'DIbaH,
mopDaj teq be' 'ej 'ang'egh be',

The trapper's father spoke,
"My son, Gilgamesh resides in Uruk.
None is stronger than he.
He is strong, like the meteor of Anu.
Go to Uruk.
Describe this man to Gilgamesh.
He will give you the harlot, Shamhat.
Bring her.
The woman will certainly conquer this man.
While the animals are drinking at the watering hole,
command the woman,
have her remove her robe and reveal herself.
When this man sees the woman, he will come close to her.
His animals will become alien."

He obeyed his father's advice.
The trapper went to Uruk.
He arrived and stood inside the city.
He explained the situation to Gilgamesh,
he said,
"A man came from the mountain.
Stronger than all.
He is strong, like the meteor of Anu.
He accompanies the animals at the watering hole.
I saw him on the other side of the watering hole.
I was afraid to get closer.
He destroys the things I make.
He sets free the animals which I trap.
He prevents me from trapping."

Gilgamesh spoke to the trapper,
"Go, trapper.
Take the harlot, Shamhat.
While the animals are drinking at the watering hole,
command her,

yIra'
be' leghDI' loDvam, be'Daq chol
novchoH Ha'DIbaHDaj>

jaH vonwI', tlhej parmaq be', Sam'at
jaj wejDIch paw
ba'
jaj wa'DIch jaj cha'DIch je bIQ DaqDaq ba'
paw Ha'DIbaHmey 'ej bIQ lutlhutlh

bIQ tlhutlhmeH ghoS, Ha'DIbaHmey tlhej,
ghaH, 'enqIyDu, HuD puq,
Ha'DIbaH tlhejbogh ghaH'e' 'ej tIr tlhol Sopbogh
bIQmo' 'ojbe', Ha'DIbaH rur
legh Sam'at, lutlh ghaH

jatlh vonwI',
<Sam'at!
ghaH 'oH Ha'DIbaHHeyvetlh'e'!
mopllj yIpoSmoH, yI'ang'egh
porghllj 'IH legh 'e' yIchaw'
DuleghDI' chol
SoHDaq QotlaHmeH mopllj yIpoSmoHchu'
lutlhwI'vamvaD be' Qu' yIta'!
ghaHvaD novchoH Ha'DIbaHDaj>

mopDaj poSmoH Sam'at, 'ang'egh,
'ej porghDaj 'IH legh
mopDaj poSmoHchu' 'ej be'Daq Qot
lutlhwI'vaD be' Qu' ta'
qaStaHvIS jav jaj parmaq be' ngagh 'enqIyDu
SeymoH be'
'ach Ha'DIbaHDaj buSchoHDI',
ghaH lulegh Ha'DIbaH 'ej DoH
'enqIyDuvo' qet Ha'DIbaH

have her remove her robe and reveal herself.
When this man sees the woman, he will come close.
His animals will become alien."

The trapper went. The harlot, Shamhat, accompanied him.
On the third day they arrived.
They sat down.
First day and second day, they sat at the watering hole.
The animals arrived and they drank the water.

He came to drink the water. He accompanied the animals.
He, Enkidu, offspring of the mountain,
he which accompanies the animals and eats the grass.
Like an animal, he quenched his thirst with water.
Shamhat saw him. He was primitive.

The trapper spoke,
"Shamhat!
That is he!
Open your robe, reveal yourself.
Permit him to see your beautiful body.
When he sees you he will draw near.
Completely open your robe so that he may lie upon you.
Perform the task of women for this primitive!
His animals will become alien to him."

Shamhat opened her robe, revealing herself,
and he saw her beautiful body.
She spread out her robe and he lay upon her.
She performed the task of women for the primitive.
For six days and nights Enkidu made love to the harlot.
The woman excited him.
But when he turned his focus to his animals,
the animals saw him and backed away.
The animals ran from Enkidu.

Doy'qu' 'enqIyDu,
Ha'DIbaHDaj tlhej luneH qIvDu'Daj, 'ach luj
qettaHvIS Ha'DIbaH rurbe'
loD moj ghaH, Qamchu', ghur SovDaj
tlhe' 'ej parmaq be' qamDaq ba'
be' qab legh, be' ghogh lubuS teSDaj

'enqIyDuvaD jatlh be',
<bI'IH, 'enqIyDu, Qun DarurchoH
qatlh Ha'DIbaH Datlhej 'ej HatlhDaq bIleng?

Ha', 'uruqDaq qaqem 'e' yIchaw'
chIrgh quv, Daq'e' luDabbogh 'anu 'IStar je,
ghIlghameS Daq,
valchu'wI', 'ach nuvpu' SeHbogh ghaH, targh naS rur,
Daqvam wIghoS>

lubelmoH mu'mey jatlhtaHbogh
Sov'eghchoH, jup nejtaH
be'vaD jatlh 'enqIyDu,
<Ha', Sam'at
HInge'
chIrgh quv, Daq'e' luDabbogh 'anu 'IStar je,
ghIlghameS Daq,
valchu'wI', 'ach nuvpu' SeHbogh ghaH, targh naS rur,
Daqvam wIghoS
ghaH vIqaD jIH
'uruqDaq jIjach, jIjatlh [jIHoSchu' jIH!]
'e' yIchaw'
HIDev 'ej tlham vIchoH jIH
HatlhDaq boghbogh ghaH HoS law Hoch HoS puS!>

jatlh Sam'at,
<Ha', qabIIj leghmeH majaH
ghIlghameSDaq qaDev, Daq vISov
'enqIyDu, 'uruq qoD yIlegh

Enkidu was very tired.
His knees wanted to accompany his animals, but failed.
He was not like the animals when he ran.
He became a man, stood tall, his knowledge broadened.
He turned and sat at the harlot's feet.
He saw the woman's face, his ear concentrated on her voice.

The woman spoke to Enkidu,
"You are beautiful, Enkidu. You become like a god.
Why do you accompany the animals
and wander in the wilderness?
Come, let me bring you to Uruk,
to the holy temple, the dwelling of Anu and Ishtar,
the place of Gilgamesh,
who is most wise, but controls the people like a fierce boar.
We will go."

The words she kept saying pleased him.
He became to know himself, he sought a friend.
Enkidu spoke to the woman,
"Come, Shamhat.
Take me away,
to the holy temple, the dwelling of Anu and Ishtar,
the place of Gilgamesh,
who is most wise, but controls the people like a fierce boar.
We will go there.
I will challenge him.
Let me shout out in Uruk,
'I am the mighty one!'
Lead me and I will change the order of things.
He which was born in the wilderness is mightiest!"

Shamhat spoke,
"Come, let's go so that he may see your face.
I will lead you to Gilgamesh, I know the place.
Enkidu, see the inside of Uruk.

lop jaj bIH Hoch jaj'e'
Supghew DIr 'In je luchu'lu'taH
parmaq be'pu' lutu'lu', HaghtaH
SoHvaD ghIlghameS vI'agh
ghaH yIlegh, qabDaj yIleghqu'
'IH
pem ram joq Qongbe'DI',
ghaH HoS law' SoH HoS puS
'enqIyDu, bIQubtaHvIS bImuj, bIchoHnIS!
ghIlghameS SaHqu' SamaS
luSovqu'moH 'anu 'enIII 'Iy'a je
HuDvo' DaghoSpa' najtaHvIS Dulegh ghIlghameS>

Hu' ghIlghameS
'ej najtaHvIS qaSbogh wanI' 'ang,
SoSDajvaD jatlh,
<SoS, jInajpu'
nargh Hovmey
jIH retlhDaq pum 'anu chunDab
vIpep 'e' vInID, 'ach 'ughqu'
vIyoymoH 'e' vInID, 'ach vIvIHmoHlaHbe'
SaH roghvaH Hoch
ghom loDpu'
'ej luquvmoH, ghu rur
muDuQ 'ej vI'uchqu', be'nal rur
qamIIjDaq vIlan
'oH jIH je ju'ovmoH>

ghIlghameSvaD jatlh,
nInSun, ghIlghameS SoS, valwI', Sovchu'wI',
<narghbogh Hovmey
SoH retlhDaq pumbogh 'anu chunDab
Dapep 'e' DanID, 'ach 'ughqu'
DayoymoH 'e' DanID, 'ach DavIHmoHlaHbe'

Every day is a day of celebration.
The lyre and drum are continually played.
There are women of love, full of laughter.
I will show you Gilgamesh.
Look at him, Look at his face.
He is handsome.
When he does not sleep day or night,
he is stronger than you.
Enkidu, you are wrong when you think. You must change!
It is Gilgamesh whom Shamash truly cares for.
Anu, Enlil, and Ea make him knowledgeable.
Before you came from the mountain,
Gilgamesh saw you in a dream."

Gilgamesh got up,
and told his mother about a dream,
"Mother, I had a dream.
The stars appeared.
The meteor of Anu fell beside me.
I tried to lift it, but it was very heavy.
I tried to turn it over, but was unable to move it.
All of the population was present.
The men gathered around.
And they honored it, like a baby.
I loved it and embraced it like a wife.
I placed it at your feet.
You made us compete."

Ninsun, mother of Gilgamesh, the wise, all-knowing,
said to Gilgamesh,
"The stars which appeared,
the meteor of Anu which fell beside you,
you tried to lift it, but it was too heavy,
you tried to turn it over, but could not,

qamwIjDaq Dalan
'oH SoH je Sa'ovmoH
'ej DuDuQ 'ej Da'uchqu', be'nal rur
vImugh
SoH DughoS loD HoS, jupDaj toDbogh maqoch'e'
ghaH HoS law' Hoch HoS puS
'anu chunDab rur HoSDaj
DuDuQ 'ej Da'uchqu', be'nal rur
DutoDqa'taH ghaH
QaQ leSSovlIj 'ej Do'!>

SoSDajvaD jatlhqa' ghIlghameS,
<SoS, jInajqa'
tlhogh pa'wIj lojmItDaq 'obmaQ tu'lu'
ghom nuvpu'
ghom roghvaH Hoch
qamlIjDaq vIlan
muDuQ 'ej vI'uchqu', be'nal rur
'ej 'oH jIH je ju'ovmoH>

ghIlghameSvaD jatlh,
nInSun, ghIlghameS SoS, valwI', Sovchu'wI',
<loD 'oS 'obmaQ Daleghbogh
ghoS loD HoS, jupDaj toDbogh maqoch'e'
ghaH HoS law' Hoch HoS puS
HoS, 'anu chunDab rur>

SoSDajvaD jatlh ghIlghameS,
<ra'mo' 'enlII, qaSjaj!
jup qeSwI' je vIghajjaj!
jIHvaD jInajtaHvIS qaSbogh wanI' Damugh!>

naj ghIlghameS 'e' ja'ta'DI' parmaq be',
nga'chuq

you placed it at my feet,
I made you compete,
and you loved it and embraced it like a wife.
I translate,
A mighty man will come to you, a comrade who saves his friend.
He is the strongest of all.
His strength is like the meteor of Anu.
You will love him and embrace him like a wife.
He will repeatedly save you.
Your dream is good and it is fortunate!"

Again Gilgamesh spoke to his mother,
"Mother, I had another dream.
There was an ax at the door to my marriage chamber.
The people gathered around.
All of the population gathered.
I placed it at your feet.
I loved it and embraced it like a wife.
And you made us compete."

Ninsun, mother of Gilgamesh, the wise, all-knowing,
spoke to Gilgamesh,
"The ax you saw is a man.
A mighty man will come, a comrade that will save his friend.
He is the strongest.
He is strong like the meteor of Anu."

Gilgamesh said to his mother,
"Because Enlil commands it, may it happen!
May I have a friend and adviser!
You have translated my dreams for me!"

When the harlot finished telling about the dreams of Gilgamesh,
they made love.

nagh beQ cha'

be' tlhopDaq ba' 'enqIyDu
SutDaj teq Sam'at
tuQmeH 'enqIyDuvaD wa' 'ay' nob,
'ej latlh 'ay' tuQ
'enqIyDu ghop 'uch Sam'at, 'ej Dev, puq rur,
Ha'DIbaH QorghwI' juHDaq qem

'enqIyDu luDech Ha'DIbaH QorghwI'
SIv 'ej ja''egh,
<ghIlghameS rur loDvam Qup
runHa'
HuDDaq boghbej
HoS, 'anu chunDab rur!>

ghaH tlhopDaq Soj lulan,
ghaH tlhopDaq HIq lulan
Sopbe' 'enqIyDu 'ej tlhutlhbe'
'ach bejqu' neH
Soj vutlu'bogh Sovbe' 'enqIyDu
HIq tlhutlhmeH tIgh ghojpu'be'

'enqIyDuvaD jatlh Sam'at,
<Soj yISop, 'enqIyDu, nuyInmoH
HIq yItlhutlh, nugh tIgh 'oH>

Soj Sopchu' 'enqIyDu
HIq tlhutlhchu'
Soch bal
mI'choH 'ej wup
chech

porghDajDaq bIQ jaD,
'ej noSvaghmey ngoH,
'ej Human moj
Sut tuQ 'ej SuvwI' rurchoH

Tablet II

Enkidu sat in front of the woman.

Shamhat removed her clothing.

She gave one item of clothing to Enkidu for him to wear,
and she wore the other piece.

Shamhat held Enkidu's hand and led him, like a child.

She brought him to the shepherd's home.

The shepherds surrounded Enkidu.

They wondered and told themselves,

"This young man resembles Gilgamesh.

He is tall.

Surely he was born in the mountains.

He is strong, like the meteor of Anu!"

They placed food in front of him.

They placed beer in front of him.

Enkidu did not eat and did not drink,
but only stared.

Enkidu did not know of cooked food.

He had not been taught the custom of drinking beer.

Shamhat spoke to Enkidu,

"Eat the food, Enkidu, it makes us live.

Drink the beer, it is the custom of society."

Enkidu devoured the food.

He drank the beer;

seven jugs.

He began to dance and burst into song.

He was drunk.

He splashed water on his body,

and smeared on deodorants,

and became human.

He put on clothes and became like a warrior.

nuH tlhap 'ej vIghro"a' tlha',
vaj qaStaHvIS ram   leSlaH QorghwI'pu'
Ha'DIbaHchaj QanmeH   Ha'DIbaH naS tlha'
'avtaHvIS 'enqIyDu   QotlaH QorghwI'pu'

qetbogh loD legh 'enqIyDu
parmaq be'vaD jatlh,
<Sam'at, loDvetlh yImejmoH!
qatlh ghoS?>

loDvaD jach Sam'at 'ej ghaH ghoS,
jatlh,
<loD Qup, nuqDaq DaghoS?
qatlh nom bIghoS?>

'enqIyDuvaD jatlh loD Qup,
<tlhogh tay vIghoS
nuv tIgh 'oH
parmaqqay wIvlu'ta'
Sanmo' be'nalvam ngagh ghIlghameS
wa'DIch ghaH,
rInDI' be'nal ghajlaH loDnal
tIghvam cher 'anu
boghDI' SanDaj 'oH tayvam'e'>

ja'DI' loD Qup QeHchoH 'enqIyDu
ghoS 'enqIyDu 'ej tlhej Sam'at

'uruq lojmIt vegh
HoSghaj
He bot

SaH roghvaH Hoch
ghom Hoch
'ej luquvmoH, ghu rur

He took a weapon and chased lions,
thus, at night the shepherds were able to rest.
He chased the wild animals to protect their herds.
While Enkidu guarded, the shepherds could lie down.

Enkidu saw a man running.
He said to the harlot,
"Shamhat, make that man leave!
Why has he come?"

Shamhat called out to the man and went over to him.
She said,
"Young man, where are you going?
Why do you go so quickly?"

The young man said to Enkidu,
"I'm going to a marriage ceremony.
It is the custom of the people.
A mate has been chosen.
Gilgamesh will mate with this wife, as is his destined right,
he will be the first man.
When he is done, the husband may have the wife.
This custom was set forth by Anu.
This right was his destiny from birth."

When the young man said this, Enkidu became angry.
Enkidu went and Shamhat accompanied him.

He advanced through the gate to Uruk.
He was powerful.
He blocked the path.

All of the populace was there.
Everyone gathered around.
And they honored him, like a baby.

tlhogh pa' lojmIt bot 'enqIyDu
'el ghIlghameS 'e' chaw'Qo'
lojmItDaq SuvchoH
HIvchuq
lam lupuvmoH qamchaj
qIp ro'Du'
HoSqu' cha' loD
QaplaH pagh
qaStaHvIS poH nI' Suvchuq
Doy'qu'choH
yavDaq ba'taHvIS leghchuqchu'
HaghchoH
'uchchuq
jup moj 'enqIyDu ghIlghameS je
maqoch

ghIlghameS ghoS 'enqIyDu
ja' 'enqIyDu,
<jupwI'
pujchoH HomwIj, Sab HoSwIj
maqanchoH>

qech chup ghIlghameS,
jatlh,
<SIyDIr ngem wIleng
Humbaba, ngem 'avwI', wIHoH
'ej SIyDIr Dun wIpe'>

qechvam par 'enqIyDu
qIHvIplaw'
ja' 'enqIyDu,
<SIyDIr ngem QanmeH,
'avwI' gheS Humbaba 'e' qaSmoH 'enlll
qu' Humbaba, naS!
SoD 'oH Humbaba bey'e'!

Enkidu blocked the door to the marriage chamber.
He refused to allow Gilgamesh to enter.
They began to fight in the entryway.
They attacked each other,
their feet kicking up dirt.
Fists striking.
The two men were very strong.
Neither was able to succeed.
They fought for a long time.
They became very tired.
Sitting on the ground, they stared at each other.
They began to laugh.
They embraced each other.
Enkidu and Gilgamesh became friends,
comrades.

Enkidu went to Gilgamesh.
Enkidu told him,
"My friend,
my bones become weak, my strength deteriorates.
We are getting old."

Gilgamesh suggested an idea,
he said,
"Let us journey to the Cedar Forest.
We will kill Humbaba, Guardian of the Forest.
And we will cut down the great Cedar."

Enkidu did not like this idea.
He was afraid.
Enkidu told him,
"To protect the Cedar Forest,
Enlil assigned Humbaba as Guardian.
Humbaba is fierce, vicious!
Humbaba's howl is a flood!

qul 'oH nujDaj'e'!
Hegh 'oH tlhuHDaj'e'!
cha'vatlh qell'qam 'abbogh chuqDaq
vIHbogh vay' QoylaH!
ngemDaj ghoSbogh vay' roSHa'moHlu'!>

'enqIyDuvaD jatlh ghIlghameS,
<jupwI'
qo'vamvo' SallaH 'Iv?
reH SamaS lutlhejlaH Qun neH
'a HumanvaD jajchaj lutoghlu'ta'
SuS lurur chavmeychaj!
DaH bIHeghvIp
bIjaqHa'choH, HoSlIj DaHutlh
jIghoS 'ej chotlha',
'ej jachlaH nujlIj, jatlh,
[yIchol, yIghoSvIpQo'!]
jIHeghchugh, jInoychoHta'
maqlu', jatlhlu',
[Humbaba, naSwI', qaDchu'ta' ghIlghameS'e'!]
HatlhDaq   bIbogh 'ej bInenchoH,
SoHDaq Sup targh, vaj Hoch DaSIQpu'!
Qu'vam vISIQ 'ej SIyDIr vIpe'chu' jIH
reH jInoychu' jIH!
Ha', jupwI', nuH po'wI' Daq vIghoS
maSaHtaHvIS nuHmaj chenmoH!>

nuH po'wI' Daq lughoS

ba' nuH chenmoHwI'pu' 'ej ja'chuq
nuHna' chenmoHchu'

'uruq loDpu'vaD jatlh ghIlghameS,
<HIQoy loDpu', tlhIH, 'uruq loD
jIDunchoH vIneH

His mouth is fire!

His breath is death!

From 100 leagues away
he can hear someone moving!

Anyone who enters his forest is paralyzed!"

Gilgamesh said to Enkidu,

"My friend,

Who can ascend from this world?

Only the gods can accompany Shamash forever.

But for humans, their days are numbered.

Their achievements are like the wind!

Now you are afraid to die.

You are no longer bold. You lack your strength.

I will go and you will follow me,

and your mouth will be able to shout out,

'Get closer, don't be afraid to go!'

If I die I will have become famous.

They will proclaim,

'It was Gilgamesh who challenged Humbaba the Terrible!'

You were born and raised in the wilderness,

a boar leaped upon you, thus you have endured all!

I will endure this and I will cut down the Cedar.

I will be famous forever!

Come, my friend, I will go to the place of the weapons experts.

They will create our weapons in our presence!"

They went to the place of the weapons experts.

The weapon smiths sat and discussed.

They engineered the finest weapons.

Gilgamesh spoke to the men of Uruk,

"Hear me men, you, men of Uruk.

I want to become great,

'ej leng nI' vIleng!
may' Qatlh vISIQ
He vIghoSpu'be'bogh vIghoS!>

quppu'vaD jatlh 'enqIyDu,
<ghIlghameSvaD pejatlh,
[SIyDIr ngem yIghoSQo']
leng ta'be'nIS!
naS SIyDIr ngem 'avwI'
SoD 'oH Humbaba bey'e'!
qul 'oH nujDaj'e'!
Hegh 'oH tlhuHDaj'e'!
cha'vatlh qell'qam 'abbogh chuqDaq
vIHbogh vay' QoylaH!
SIyDIr ngem QanmeH,
'avwI' gheS Humbaba 'e' qaSmoH 'enIII>

Hu' 'uruq yej quv 'ej ghIlghameS luqeS, jatlh,
<bIQup, ghIlghameS, Duqeng tIqllj
qaDllj Dayajchu'be'!
SoD 'oH Humbaba bey'e'!
qul 'oH nujDaj'e'!
Hegh 'oH tlhuHDaj'e'!
cha'vatlh qell'qam 'abbogh chuqDaq
vIHbogh vay' QoylaH!
SIyDIr ngem QanmeH,
'avwI' gheS Humbaba 'e' qaSmoH 'enIII>

yejDaj quv qeS Qoy ghIlghameS

and I will travel a lengthy voyage!
I will endure difficult battle.
I will travel a road I have never traveled before!"

Enkidu spoke to the elders,
"Say to Gilgamesh,
'Don't go to the Cedar Forest.'
He must not make this journey!
The guardian of the Cedar Forest is vicious.
The howl of Humbaba is a flood!
His mouth is fire!
His breath is death!
From 100 leagues away,
he can hear someone moving!
To protect the Cedar Forest,
Enlil assigned Humbaba as Guardian."

The Honored Council of Uruk got up and advised Gilgamesh,
"You are young, Gilgamesh, your heart carries you.
You do not completely understand your challenge!
The howl of Humbaba is a flood!
His mouth is fire!
His breath is death!
From 100 leagues away
he can hear someone moving!
To protect the Cedar Forest,
Enlil assigned Humbaba as Guardian."

Gilgamesh listened to the advice of his Honored Council.

nagh beQ wej

ghIlghameSvaD jatlh qup,
<ghIlghameS, HoSIIj neH yIvoqQo',
'ach mInIlj tIpoSmoHchu'
DoS tIqIpchu'!
maqoch choq tlhegh tlhopDaq yItbogh loD'e'
jupDaj Qan   He Sovbogh loD'e'
Dev 'enqIyDu 'e' yIchaw' 'ej yItlha'
SIyDIr ngem He Sov ghaH
vIq SIQ ghaH
jup Qan 'enqIyDu, maqoch choq>

'enqIyDuvaD jatlh qup,
<voDleH DaQanmeH pIvoq
bIcheghDI' maHvaD voDleHma' DanobHa'!>

'enqIyDuvaD jatlh ghIlghameS,
<Ha', jupwI', 'IyghaIma chIrgh wIghoS,
nInSun, joH Dun, wIghoS
val nInSun, Hoch Sov
nuqeS>

yIt ghIlghameS 'enqIyDu je,
'IyghaIma chIrgh lughoS
nInSun, joH Dun, lughoS
jatlh,
<nInSun, jIHoSqu'
DaH Humbaba Daq vIlengnIS
tIqqu' He
may' Qatlh vISIQnIS
He vISovbe'bogh vIlengnIS
jIDachtaHvIS,
SIyDIr ngem vIghoStaHvIS,
Humbaba mIgh vISuvtaHvIS,
'ej vay"e' muSbogh SamaS vIQaw'taHvIS,

Tablet III

The elders spoke to Gilgamesh,
"Gilgamesh, don't trust only your strength,
but open your eyes.
Hit the target!
The man that walks in front saves the comrade.
The man that knows the path protects his friend.
Let Enkidu lead and you follow.
He knows the path to the Cedar Forest.
He has endured combat.
Enkidu will protect a friend, he will save the comrade."

The elders spoke to Enkidu,
"We trust you to protect the king.
When you return you will give our king back to us!"

Gilgamesh spoke to Enkidu,
"Come, my friend, we will go to the Egalmah temple.
We will go to Ninsun, the Great Queen.
Ninsun is wise, all-knowing.
She will advise us."

Gilgamesh and Enkidu walked.
They went to the Egalmah temple.
They went to Ninsun, the Great Queen.
He said,
"Ninsun, I am very strong.
Now I need to travel to the place of Humbaba.
The path is very long.
I will need to endure difficult battle.
I need to travel a road I have never traveled before.
While I am absent,
while I am going to the Cedar Forest,
while I am fighting the evil Humbaba,
and while I destroy what Shamash hates,

jIHvaD SamaS yIqoy'!
Humbaba vIHoHchugh 'ej SIyDIrDaj vIpe'chugh,
Dat wup Hoch 'ej lop   'e' tu'lu',
'ej yay 'oSmeH Hew vIchenmoH!>

puqloDDaj mu' Qoyqa'taH nInSun joH 'IQ

juHDaj 'el nInSun
Say"eghmoH
mop tuQmoH
ghIgh tuQmoH
Ha'qujDaj tuQmoH, 'ej mIv'a'Daj tuQmoH
maHpIn tlhap 'ej yavDaq bIQ ghomHa'moH
beb ghoS, lat ghoS,
'ej SamaS tlhopDaq meQbogh naQHom quv lan
SamaSvaD DeSDaj pepneS
jatlh,
<qatlh ghIlghameSvaD tIq ngoj Danobta'?
DaH DaSIgh,
vaj HumbabaDaq He tIq leng   neH!
may' Qatlh tu'
'ej He Sovbe'bogh leng!
DachtaHvIS,
SIyDIr ngem ghoStaHvIS,
Humbaba mIgh SuvtaHvIS,
'ej vay' DamuSbogh Qaw'taHvIS,
DuqawvIpbe'moHjaj 'aja', naywI',
'ej ram bejwI'pu' Hovmey je ra'jaj 'aja',
'ej qaStaHvIS ram vavlI', SIn ra'jaj 'aja'>

meQbogh naQHom quv lanqa' nInSun,
'ej mu' SeQ jatlh
qeSmeH 'enqIyDuvaD jatlh
'enqIyDu mongDaq ghIgh le' lan

plead to Shamash for me!
If I kill Humbaba and if I cut his Cedar,
everywhere everyone will burst into song and celebration,
and I will create a statue of victory!"

The grieving Queen Ninsun heard over and over
the words of her son.
Ninsun entered her home.
She washed herself.
She put on a robe.
She put on a necklace.
She put on her sash, and her crown.
She took a bowl and scattered water on the ground.
She went up to the roof, over to the shrine,
and placed incense in front of Shamash.
She raised her arms to Shamash.
She said,
"Why did you give Gilgamesh a restless heart?
Now you influence him,
thus he wants to travel the long road to Humbaba!
He will find difficult battles.
And he will travel unknown roads!
While he is absent,
while he is going to the Cedar Forest,
while he fights the evil Humbaba,
and while he destroys what you hate,
may Aja, the Bride, not be afraid to remind you,
and may Aja command the stars and the watchers of the night,
and during the night may Aja command your father, Sin."

Ninsun again placed incense,
and spoke the ceremonial words.
She advised Enkidu.
She placed a pendant on Enkidu's neck.

'enqIyDu quvmoH nInSun
'ej Qun qoy'neS

Ninsun honored Enkidu.
And she prayed to the gods.

nagh beQ loS

vaghmaH qell'qam lengta'DI' SopmeH mev
SochmaH vagh qell'qam lengta'DI' QongmeH mev
qaStaHvIS pem naQ yIt,
wa'vatlh cha'maH vagh qell'qam ghoS
jaj wejDIch lebanan luchol

SamaS lurghDaq bIQ HaI luchenmoH
HuD toS ghIlghameS
Qun quvmoHmeH yavDaq tIr lIch, 'ej jatlh,
<HuD, HInajmoH
SamaSvo' QIn qaq vIHevjaj>

QongmeH Daq cher 'enqIyDu
SuS ral tu'lu'mo' reDHom chenmoH
Qot, 'ej QongchoH

ramjep vem ghIlghameS, vaj Hu',
'ej jupDajvaD jatlh,
<jupwI', jIHvaD bIjatlh'a'?
qatlh jIvem?
choHot'a'?
qatlh jIbIt?
nujuS'a' Qun?
qatlh Qom SomrawwIj?
'enqIyDu, jupwI', jInaj
jInajtaHvIS ghu'mo' 'anglu'bogh jIbItqu'!
ngechDaq jIHDaq pum HuD
nutap, ghew rur>

wanI' 'anglu'bogh mugh 'enqIyDu,
jatlh,
<jupwI', qaq bInajtaHvIS ghu"e' Daqelbogh
potlh wanI'vam
jupwI', Humbaba 'oS HuD Daleghbogh

Tablet IV

After twenty leagues they stopped to eat.
After thirty leagues they stopped to sleep.
They walked a whole day,
going fifty leagues.
On the third day they came near Lebanan.

They dug a well in the direction of Shamash.
Gilgamesh climbed a mountain.
He poured grain on the ground to appease the gods, and said,
"Mountain, give me a dream.
May I receive a favorable message from Shamash."

Enkidu setup a place to sleep.
He made a windbreaker because there was a violent wind.
They lied down, and went to sleep.

In the middle of the night Gilgamesh awoke, so he got up,
and said to his friend,
"My friend, did you say something to me?
Why did I wake up?
Did you touch me?
Why am I uneasy?
Did a god pass us?
Why are my muscles trembling?
Enkidu, my friend, I had a dream.
I am very disturbed by what happened in my dream!
A mountain fell on me in a valley.
It squashed us like bugs."

Enkidu interpreted the dream,
he said,
"My friend, your dream is favorable.
This dream is important.
My friend, the mountain you saw was Humbaba.

Humbaba wIjon 'ej wIHoH,
'ej ghe''orDaq lomDaj wIwoD
po SamaSvo' QIn Do' tu'lu' >

vaghmaH qell'qam lengta'DI' SopmeH mev
SochmaH vagh qell'qam lengta'DI' QongmeH mev
qaStaHvIS pem naQ yIt,
wa'vatlh cha'maH vagh qell'qam ghoS

SamaS lurghDaq bIQ Hal luchenmoH
HuD toS ghIlghameS
Qun quvmoHmeH yavDaq tIr lIch, 'ej jatlh,
<HuD, HInajmoH
SamaSvo' QIn qaq vIHevjaj>

QongmeH Daq cher 'enqIyDu
SuS ral tu'lu'mo' reDHom chenmoH
Qot, 'ej QongchoH

ramjep vem ghIlghameS, vaj Hu',
'ej jupDajvaD jatlh,
<jupwI', jIHvaD bIjatlh'a'?
qatlh jIvem?
choHot'a'?
qatlh jIbIt?
nujuS'a' Qun?
qatlh Qom SomrawwIj?
'enqIyDu, jupwI'
jInajpu' 'ej jInajqa'
jInajtaHvIS ghu'mo' 'anglu'bogh jIbItqu'!
Ha'DIbaH naS vISuv
yav poSmoH beyDaj
chal teb lamHom 'eng
ghaH tlhopDaq qIvwIjDaq jIDej
HuS jatwIj

We will capture Humbaba and kill him,
and we will throw his corpse into Hell.
In the morning there will be a favorable message from Shamash."

After twenty leagues they stopped to eat.
After thirty leagues they stopped to sleep.
They walked a whole day,
going fifty leagues.

They dug a well in the direction of Shamash.
Gilgamesh climbed a mountain.
He poured grain on the ground to appease the gods, and said,
"Mountain, give me a dream.
May I receive a favorable message from Shamash."

Enkidu setup a place to sleep.
He made a windbreaker because there was a violent wind.
They lied down, and went to sleep.

In the middle of the night Gilgamesh awoke, so he got up,
and said to his friend,
"My friend, did you say something to me?
Why did I wake up?
Did you touch me?
Why am I uneasy?
Did a god pass us?
Why are my muscles trembling?
Enkidu, my friend,
I had another dream.
I am very disturbed by what happened in my dream!
I fought a vicious animal.
His howl opened the ground.
A cloud of dust filled the sky.
I collapsed to my knees in front of him.
My tongue hanging.

'oy'chu' nachwIj
vItlhutlhmeH DIr balvo' bIQ munob>

mugh 'enqIyDu, jatlh,
<jupwI',
Qun wIghoSbogh 'oSbe' Ha'DIbaH naS!
pImchu' ghaH!
SamaS, QanwI', 'oSba' Ha'DIbaH naS Daleghbogh
QatlhtaHvIS ghu' ghopmaj 'uch ghaH
DuquvmoHbogh joH'a'lI', lughalbanDa,
'oSbej SoHvaD DIr balvo' bIQ nobbogh ghaH'e'
matay'nISchoH,
'ej wa' Qu', Qu"e' not ta'lu'bogh, wIta'nIS>

vaghmaH qell'qam lengta'DI' SopmeH mev
SochmaH vagh qell'qam lengta'DI' QongmeH mev
qaStaHvIS pem naQ   yIt,
wa'vatlh cha'maH vagh qell'qam ghoS

SamaS lurghDaq bIQ Hal luchenmoH
HuD toS ghIlghameS
Qun quvmoHmeH yavDaq tIr lIch, 'ej jatlh,
<HuD, HInajmoH
SamaSvo' QIn qaq vIHevjaj>

QongmeH Daq cher 'enqIyDu
SuS ral tu'lu'mo' reDHom chenmoH
Qot, 'ej QongchoH

ramjep vem ghIlghameS, vaj Hu',
'ej jupDajvaD jatlh,
<jupwI', jIHvaD bIjatlh'a'?
qatlh jIvem?
choHot'a'?
qatlh jIbIt?

My head throbbing.
He gave me water to drink from a waterskin."

Enkidu interpreted,
"My friend,
The vicious animal is not the god to which we go!
He is totally different!
The vicious animal you saw is obviously Shamash, the protector.
During difficulties he holds our hand.
He which gives you water from the waterskin,
is certainly your god, which brings you honor, Lugalbanda.
We need to join together,
and we must accomplish one task,
a task which has never been done."

After twenty leagues they stopped to eat.
After thirty leagues they stopped to sleep.
They walked a whole day,
going fifty leagues.

They dug a well in the direction of Shamash.
Gilgamesh climbed a mountain.
He poured grain on the ground to appease the gods, and said,
"Mountain, give me a dream.
May I receive a favorable message from Shamash."

Enkidu setup a place to sleep.
He made a windbreaker because there was a violent wind.
They lied down, and went to sleep.

In the middle of the night Gilgamesh awoke, so he got up,
and said to his friend,
"My friend, did you say something to me?
Why did I wake up?
Did you touch me?
Why am I uneasy?

nujuS'a' Qun?
qatlh Qom SomrawwIj?
'enqIyDu, jupwI', cha'logh jInajpu' 'ej jInajqa'
jInajtaHvIS ghu'mo' 'anglu'bogh jIbItqu'!
jach chal 'ej Qom yav
tamchoH Hoch 'ej vIHbe', Hegh rur
HurghchoH
'ul baHlu'
qul tu'lu'
Hegh tu'lu'
rIn qul
lam moj pumpu'bogh Hoch
yotlhDaq HItlhej, maja'chuqmeH>

ghIlghameS Qoy 'enqIyDu
'ej wanI' mugh 'enqIyDu

vaghmaH qell'qam lengta'DI' SopmeH mev
SochmaH vagh qell'qam lengta'DI' QongmeH mev
qaStaHvIS pem naQ   yIt,
wa'vatlh cha'maH vagh qell'qam ghoS

SamaS lurghDaq bIQ HaI luchenmoH
HuD toS ghIlghameS
Qun quvmoHmeH yavDaq tIr lIch, 'ej jatlh,
<HuD, HInajmoH
SamaSvo' QIn qaq vIHevjaj>

QongmeH Daq cher 'enqIyDu
SuS ral tu'lu'mo' reDHom chenmoH
Qot, 'ej QongchoH

ramjep vem ghIlghameS, vaj Hu',
'ej jupDajvaD jatlh,
<jupwI', jIHvaD bIjatlh'a'?
qatlh jIvem?

Did a god pass us?
Why are my muscles trembling?
Enkidu, my friend, I had a third dream.
I am very disturbed by what happened in my dream!
The sky cried out and the ground trembled.
Everything became quiet and still, like death.
It became dark.
Lightning flashed.
There was fire.
There was death.
The fire ended.
Everything which had fallen became dirt.
Accompany me in the field, so we can discuss it."

Enkidu listened to Gilgamesh.
And Enkidu interpreted the dream.

After twenty leagues they stopped to eat.
After thirty leagues they stopped to sleep.
They walked a whole day,
going fifty leagues.

They dug a well in the direction of Shamash.
Gilgamesh climbed a mountain.
He poured grain on the ground to appease the gods, and said,
"Mountain, give me a dream.
May I receive a favorable message from Shamash."

Enkidu setup a place to sleep.
He made a windbreaker because there was a violent wind.
They lied down, and went to sleep.

In the middle of the night Gilgamesh awoke, so he got up,
and said to his friend,
"My friend, did you say something to me?
Why did I wake up?

choHot'a'?
qatlh jIbIt?
nujuS'a' Qun?
qatlh Qom Somrawwlj?
'enqIyDu, jupwI', wejlogh jInajpu' 'ej jInajqa'
jInajtaHvIS ghu'mo' 'anglu'bogh jIbItqu'!>

QIjtaHvIS ghIlghameS   Qoy 'enqIyDu

jatlh 'enqIyDu,
<jupwI', qaq bInajtaHvIS ghu''e' Daqelbogh
potlh wanI'vam
qaSpa' jajlo' yay wIchav
Humbaba wIjeybej
wIQaw'chu'
po SamaSvo' QIn Do' tu'lu'>

vaghmaH qelI'qam lengta'DI' SopmeH mev
SochmaH vagh qelI'qam lengta'DI' QongmeH mev
qaStaHvIS pem naQ yIt,
wa'vatlh cha'maH vagh qelI'qam ghoS

SamaS lurghDaq bIQ Hal luchenmoH
HuD toS ghIlghameS
Qun quvmoHmeH yavDaq tIr lIch, 'ej jatlh,
<HuD, HInajmoH
SamaSvo' QIn qaq vIHevjaj>

QongmeH Daq cher 'enqIyDu
SuS ral tu'lu'mo' reDHom chenmoH
Qot, 'ej QongchoH

ramjep vem ghIlghameS, vaj Hu',
'ej jupDajvaD jatlh,
<jupwI', jIHvaD bIjatlh'a'?
qatlh jIvem?

Did you touch me?
Why am I uneasy?
Did a god pass us?
Why are my muscles trembling?
Enkidu, my friend, I had a fourth dream.
I am very disturbed by what happened in my dream!"

While Gilgamesh explained, Enkidu listened.

Enkidu said,
"My friend, your dream is favorable.
This dream is important.
By dawn we will achieve victory.
We will certainly defeat Humbaba.
We will completely destroy him.
In the morning there will be a favorable message from Shamash."

After twenty leagues they stopped to eat.
After thirty leagues they stopped to sleep.
They walked a whole day,
going fifty leagues.

They dug a well in the direction of Shamash.
Gilgamesh climbed a mountain.
He poured grain on the ground to appease the gods, and said,
"Mountain, give me a dream.
May I receive a favorable message from Shamash."

Enkidu setup a place to sleep.
He made a windbreaker because there was a violent wind.
They lied down, and went to sleep.

In the middle of the night Gilgamesh awoke, so he got up,
and said to his friend,
"My friend, did you say something to me?
Why did I wake up?

choHot'a'?
qatlh jIbIt?
nujuS'a' Qun?
qatlh Qom SomrawwIj?
'enqIyDu, jupwI', loSlogh jInajpu' 'ej jInajqa'
jInajtaHvIS ghu'mo' 'anglu'bogh jIbItqu'!>

Qoy 'enqIyDu
'ej wanI' mugh

SamaSvaD SaQ ghIlghameS
jatlh,
<'uruqDaq mu'mey Dajatlhbogh yIqaw
HIQaH!>

ghIlghameS, 'uruq puq, Qoy SamaS
pay' chalvo' QIch Qoylu'
jatlh,
<tugh! Humbaba yIbot
ngem 'el 'e' yIchaw'Qo'!
So"eghmeH lav ghoS 'e' yIchaw'Qo'!
Soch wepDaj tuQbe'
wa' neH tuQ,
jav teq>

Humbaba lut Sov 'enqIyDu
ngem 'elvIp

ghIlghameS QeHchoHmoH ghu'vam
'enqIyDuDaq jop ghIlghameS
Suv, targh qu' rur
Suv 'e' Qoy Humbaba, ngem 'avwI'

'enqIyDuvaD jatlh ghIlghameS,

Did you touch me?
Why am I uneasy?
Did a god pass us?
Why are my muscles trembling?
Enkidu, my friend, I had a fifth dream.
I am very disturbed by what happened in my dream!"

Enkidu listened.
And he interpreted the dream.

Gilgamesh cried for Shamash,
saying,
"Remember the words that you spoke in Uruk.
Help me!"

Shamash heard Gilgamesh, offspring of Uruk.
suddenly a voice was heard from the sky,
saying,
"Hurry! Block Humbaba.
Do not permit him to enter the forest!
Do not allow him to go into the thickets and hide!
He does not wear his seven coats.
He is wearing only one,
he has taken off six."

Enkidu knew the legends of Humbaba
He was afraid to enter the forest.

This made Gilgamesh angry
Gilgamesh lunged at Enkidu.
They fought like wild boars.
Humbaba, Guardian of the Forest, heard them fighting.

Gilgamesh spoke to Enkidu,

<wa' Dol nIvDaq matay'DI' maQap
bIHeghvIpchugh bIHeghpu'
nIteb Qob qaD jup 'e' chaw'be' SuvwI'>

ghIlghameSvaD jatlh 'enqIyDu,
<SIyDIr ngem wIghoSDI',
Sor wISIj 'ej wIpoSmoH,
'ej naQmey wIwItlh>

'enqIyDuvaD jatlh ghIlghameS,
<qatlh, jupwI'?
matay', Hoch HuD DIchargh
leng tlq wISIQ
jupwI', vIq qellu'taHvIS bIpo'qu'ba'
DaHotlu'mo' bIHeghvIpbe'
ghum ghoghlIj, 'In rur 'e' yIchaw'
vIH DeSDu'lIj 'uSDu'lIj je 'e' yIchaw'
ghopwIj yI'uch, jupwI', matay', majaH
ghobmeH 'ebmo' meQnIS tIqlIj
Hegh yIbuSQo'
qa'lIj yIchIlQo'!
loD yep ghaH Dopvo' bejbogh vay"e'
'ach maqochDaj toD 'ej Qan'egh,
tlhopDaq yItbogh loD
'ej Suvmo' noychoH chaH!>

"Together as one we can succeed.
If you are afraid to die, you are already dead.
A warrior does not allow a friend face danger alone."

Enkidu spoke to Gilgamesh,
"As soon as we go to the Cedar Forest,
we will slit the tree and open it,
and break off the branches."

Gilgamesh said to Enkidu,
"Why, my friend?
We are together, we conquered all the mountains.
We endured a long journey.
My friend, you are obviously very experienced in battle.
Because you are touched you are not afraid to die.
Let your voice sound an alarm like a drum.
Let your arms and legs move.
Hold my hand, my friend, we are together, we will go.
Your heart should burn at the opportunity to do battle.
Do not focus on death.
Do not lose your spirit!
Someone that watches from the side is a careful man.
But a man that walks in front,
saves his comrade and protects himself.
And through the fight they become famous!"

nagh beQ vagh

SIyDIr ngemDaq pawDI',
jaw 'e' mev 'ej Qam

ngem HeHDaq Qam
SIyDIr Sor lubuS
ngem HeH lubuS
He tu'lu'
HevamDaq yItta' Humbaba
pov He

SIyDIr HuD,
Daq'e' luDabbogh Qun,
'IrnIynIy Daq quv lulegh
ngem Dech wej qell'qam 'abbogh qoj

yanmeychaj 'obmaQmeychaj je woH
Sormey pe'choH
pe' 'e' Qoy Humbaba 'ej ghoS

ghIlghameSvaD jatlh Humbaba

HumbabavaD jatlh 'enqIyDu,
<wa' Dol nIvDaq matay'DI' maQap
pIjeylaH>

ghIlghameSvaD jatlh Humbaba,
<qeSchuqnIS qoH QIpwI' je
'ach SoH, ghIlghameS, qatlh choghoS?
yIqeS, 'enqIyDu, bIQDep puqloD,
vavDaj Sovbe'bogh ghaH'e'
SoS nIm tlhutlhbe'bogh Ha'DIbaH yIqeS jay'!
bIQuptaHvIS qalegh
'ach qaghoSbe'
jIHDaq ghIlghameS Daqem

Tablet V

When they arrived at the Cedar Forest,
They stopped chatting and stood.

They stood at the edge of the forest.
They gazed on the Cedar Tree.
They gazed on the edge of the forest.
There was a path.
Humbaba had walked this path.
The path was excellent.

They saw the Cedar Mountain,
the dwelling of the gods,
the honored site of Irnini.
A cliff two leagues long surrounded the forest.

They picked up their swords and their axes.
They began cutting the trees.
Humbaba heard the chopping and came.

Humbaba spoke to Gilgamesh.

Enkidu spoke to Humbaba,
"Together as one we will succeed.
We can defeat you."

Humbaba said to Gilgamesh,
"A fool and a moron must advise each other.
But you, Gilgamesh, why do you come to me?
Give advice, Enkidu, son of a fish,
he which doesn't know his father.
Give advice to animals that do not drink mother's milk!
I saw you when you were young.
But I did not go to you.
You brought Gilgamesh to me.

jagh SoH, novwI'
nISopmeH toQvaD porghIIj vInobnIS!>

qabDaj choHmoH Humbaba
moHqu'choH, veqlargh rur

'enqIyDuvaD jatlh ghIlghameS,
<jupwI', choHtaH Humbaba qab!>

ghIlghameSvaD jatlh 'enqIyDu,
<jupwI, qatlh bIvIng 'ej bISo"egh?
nuHmeymaj tIqel
nuHmeymaj nIv chenmoHchu' nuH chenmoHwI'pu' po'
yanmaj 'obmaQmaj je nIv law' Hoch nuH nIv puS
maQaplaH>

'obmaQ woH 'enqIyDu
SIyDIr pe'choH

'e' QoyDI' Humbaba QeHqu'choH
jatlh,
<ghoS 'Iv 'ej Sormey quvHa'moH 'Iv?
HuDwIj ghoS 'Iv 'ej SIyDIr pummoH 'Iv?
Sange'nIS 'ej chalvo' Sachagh
nachraj vItap 'ej yav HurghDaq Salan!>

HurghchoH 'eng chIS
SIS Hegh

SaQ ghIlghameS 'ej SamaSvaD jach

Humbaba qaD SamaS
loS lurghvo' SuS, DuQbogh SuS, SuS HoS,

SuS mIgh, SuS chuS, SImuru SuS, SuS ral,

veqlargh SuS, chuch SuS, SuS'a' je
chen wa'maH wej SuS 'ej Humbaba qab qat
'et ghoSlaHbe'

You are the enemy, the stranger.
I should feed your body to the vultures!"

Humbaba made his face change.
It became so ugly, like the devil.

Gilgamesh said to Enkidu,
"My friend, Humbaba's face keeps changing!"

Enkidu said to Gilgamesh,
"My friend, why do you whine and hide yourself?
Consider our weapons.
The expert weapon makers made our superior weapons.
Our swords and our axes are more superior than all other weapons.
We can succeed."

Enkidu picked up an axe.
He started cutting the Cedar.

When Humbaba heard this, he became very angry.
He spoke,
"Who has come and dishonored the trees?
Who has come to my mountain and caused the Cedar to fall?
I should take you away and drop you from the sky.
I will mash your heads and put you into the dark ground!"

The white clouds became dark.
Death rained down.

Gilgamesh cried and shouted out to Shamash.

Shamash confronted Humbaba.
The winds from four directions, the piercing wind,
the strong wind,
the evil wind, the noisy wind, the wind of Simurru,
the violent wind,
the demon wind, the ice wind, and the storm;
thirteen winds took form and encased the face of Humbaba.
He could not go fore.

'o' ghoSlaHbe'
vaj Humbaba SIch ghIlghameS nuH
yIntaHmeH qoy'qu' Humbaba
jatlh,
<bIQup, ghIlghameS
rIm'at-nInSun puq SoH
Qu'vamvaD DuSeymoH SamaS, HuD joH
'uruq tlq puq, ghIlghameS voDleH!
ghIlghameS, HItlhabmoH
qatoy'
SoHmo' Sormey vIpe', 'ar DaneH?>

ghIlghameSvaD jatlh 'enqIyDu,
<jupwI', Humbaba yIQoyQo'
nep ghaH>
ghIlghameS pon 'e' nID 'enqIyDu

ghIlghameS SIghlaw' 'enqIyDu 'e' legh Humbaba
jatlh Humbaba,
<ngemwIj chut Dayaj
Hoch chutmey'e' cherbogh 'enlI DaSov
ngemwIj Da'elDI' qaHoHnIS
nISopmeH toQvaD porghIj vInobnIS
vaj DaH pung HI'ang
muHoHbe'meH ghIlghameS yIpon!>

ghIlghameSvaD jatlh 'enqIyDu,
<jupwI'
Humbaba, SIyDIr ngem QanwI', yIHoH
yItap, yIQaw', yIlagh, yInDaj yInge'!
Qoypa' 'enlI 'ej maHmo' QeHchoHpa' Qunpu',
yIruch
nI'pIrDaq ghaHtaH 'enlI'e'
SI'parDaq ghaHtaH SamaS'e'
Hewna' yIchenmoH
Humbaba HoH ghIlghameS 'e' maqbogh Hew>

He could not go aft.

Thus Gilgamesh's weapon reached Humbaba.

Humbaba pleaded for his life,

saying,

"You are young, Gilgamesh.

You are the offspring of Rimat-Ninsun.

Shamash, Lord of the Mountain, made you excited for this quest.

Child of the heart of Uruk, King Gilgamesh!

Gilgamesh, let me go.

I will serve you.

I will cut the trees for you, how many do you want?"

Enkidu said to Gilgamesh,

"My friend, don't listen to Humbaba.

He is lying."

Enkidu tried to persuade Gilgamesh.

Humbaba saw that Enkidu was apparently influencing Gilgamesh.

Humbaba said,

"You understand the laws of my forest.

You know every law established by Enlil.
I should have killed you when you entered my forest.

I should feed your body to the vultures.

So now show me mercy.

Convince Gilgamesh to not kill me!"

Enkidu said to Gilgamesh,

"My friend,

kill him, Humbaba, Protector of the Cedar Forest.

Mash him, destroy him, take him apart, take away his life!

Before Enlil hears and before the gods become angry at us,

do it.

Enlil is in Nippur.

Shamash is in Sippar.

Create a monument,

a monument which proclaims that Gilgamesh killed Humbaba."

qoy'qa' Humbaba
HoHQo' ghIlghameS 'e' qoy'
ghIlghameS pon 'enqIyDu 'e' qoy'

ghIlghameSvaD jatlhqa 'enqIyDu,
<jupwI'
Humbaba, SIyDIr ngem QanwI', yIHoH
yItap, yIQaw', yIlagh, yInDaj yInge'!
Qoypa' 'enlII 'ej maHmo' QeHchoHpa' Qunpu',
yIruch
nI'pIrDaq ghaHtaH 'enlII'e'
SI'parDaq ghaHtaH SamaS'e'
Hewna' yIchenmoH
Humbaba HoH ghIlghameS 'e' maqbogh Hew>

Humbaba lughIj 'enqIyDu mu'
QeHchoH Humbaba
maQmIgh jatlh
jatlh,
<Heghjaj 'enqIyDu!
Heghpa' ghIlghameS Heghjaj 'enqIyDu!
Hegh batlhHa'!>

ghIlghameSvaD jatlh 'enqIyDu,
<jupwI'
SoHvaD jIjatlhta' 'ach choQoyQo'
Humbaba maQmIgh neH DaQoy!
yIHoH jay'!>

yev ghIlghameS
jupDaj Qoy
yanDaj pep ghIlghameS 'ej Humbaba DuQ
Humbaba pe' 'ej poSmoH
luH burgh je lel 'enqIyDu ghIlghameS je
jatDaj luteq je

Humbaba pleaded again.
He begged for Gilgamesh to not kill him.
He begged for Enkidu to persuade Gilgamesh.

Enkidu spoke again to Gilgamesh,
"My friend,
kill him, Humbaba, Protector of the Cedar Forest.
Mash him, destroy him, take him apart, take away his life!
Before Enlil hears and before the gods become angry at us,
do it.
Enlil is in Nippur.
Shamash is in Sippar.
Create a monument,
a monument which proclaims that Gilgamesh killed Humbaba."

The words of Enkidu scared Humbaba.
Humbaba became angry.
He uttered a curse,
saying,
"May Enkidu die!
May Enkidu die before Gilgamesh dies!
A dishonorable death!"

Enkidu said to Gilgamesh,
"My friend,
I have spoken to you but you do not listen to me.
You hear only the curse of Humbaba!
KILL HIM!"

Gilgamesh paused.
He listened to his friend.
Gilgamesh raised his sword and stabbed Humbaba.
He cut Humbaba and opened him up.
Enkidu and Gilgamesh took out the intestines and stomach.
They also removed his tongue.

SIyDIr pe'
Sormey pe'taHvIS ghIlghameS,
tInqu'wI' nej 'enqIyDu

jatlh 'enqIyDu,
<jupwI'
chal Hotbogh SIyDIr'e' wIpe'ta'
SIyDIrvam tIn law' Hoch tIn puS
lojmIt wIchenmoH
HutmaH 'uj 'aD
wejmaH 'uj juch
wa' vI' vagh 'uj Saw'
nI'pIrDaq luqeng
qeng yu'reytIy bIQtIq
lop nI'pIr>

DujHom luchenmoH
chIj 'enqIyDu
Humbaba nach 'uch ghIlghameS

They cut the Cedar.
While Gilgamesh cut the trees,
Enkidu looked for one that towered high.

Enkidu said,
"My friend,
we have cut the Cedar that touched the sky.
This Cedar is larger than all others.
We will make a gate.
It will measure seventy-two cubits high,
twenty-four cubits wide,
one cubit thick.
They will carry it to Nippur.
The Euphrates River will carry it.
Nippur will celebrate."

They made a raft.
Enkidu steered.
Gilgamesh held the head of Humbaba.

nagh beQ jav

jIbDaj Say'moH
luchDaj Say'moH
Sut lam teq 'ej Sut Say' tuQchoH
voDleH Sut tuQ
'ej Ha'quj rar
nachDajDaq mIv'a'Daj lanDI' ghIlghameS,
'IH ghIlghameS 'e' legh 'IStar joH
jatlh,
<Ha', ghIlghameS
HISaw
HIngagh
loDnalwI' SoH 'ej be'nallI' jIH
juHmaj yI'el
He', SIyDIr rur
SoH bIngDaq tor voDleHpu' joHpu' je
nIquvmoHmeH,
HuD naH Hatlh naH je qem lullubu nuvpu'

HoSchoH Ha'DIbaHlIj
law'choH Ha'DIbaHlIj
bIchep
bImIp
choSawchugh qaS wanI'vam>

'IStar joHvaD jatlh ghIlghameS,
<qaSawchugh nuq vInobnIS?
Sut DaSuqnIS'a'?
Soj DaHutlh'a'?
HIq Soj je vInobqang
[jISaH] juja' 'ach bISaHbe'
parmaq Qun SoH 'ach bImIgh
nuqDaq chaHtaH   SawwI'lI''e' DapoltaHbogh?
bangpu'lI' tetlh vIlaDnIS'a'?

Tablet VI

He cleaned his hair.

He cleaned his equipment.

He took off the dirty clothes and put on clean clothes.

He wore kings' clothing.

And fastened the sash.

When Gilgamesh placed his crown on his head,

Princess Ishtar saw how handsome Gilgamesh was.

She said,

"Come, Gilgamesh.

Marry me.

Mate with me.

You will be my husband and I will be your wife.

Enter our home.

It has the fragrance of cedar.

Kings and lords will kneel beneath you.

To honor you,

the Lullubu people will bring
fruit of the mountains and countryside.

Your herds will grow strong.

Your herds will become numerous.

You will prosper.

You will be wealthy.

This will be if we marry."

Gilgamesh said to Princess Ishtar,

"If I marry you, what must I give?

Do you need clothes?

Do you lack food?

I am willing to give food and wine.

You tell us you care, but you do not care.

You are the goddess of love but you are evil.

Where are your grooms that you are keeping forever?

Shall I recite the list of your lovers?

tammuj,
banglI' wa'DIch
toQ mach,
DaqIp 'ej telDaj Daghor
DaH ngemDaq Qam 'ej SaQ
vIghro"a' HoS,
'ach molqoq DachenmoH
molDaq pum
Sargh,
vIqmo' quv
DaH mup tlhegh 'ej bIQ lam tlhutlh
Ha'DIbaH Qorghwl',
Ha'DIbaH qu' moj ghaH 'e' DaqaSmoH
vaj luHoHmeH lutlha' latlh Qorghwl'pu'
'IS'ullan'u, vavlI' wIjwI',
Hoch jaj SoHvaD naH qem
lung moj ghaH 'e' DaqaSmoH
'ej DaH jIH!
jIHvaD qaS nuq?>

'e' QoyDI' 'IStar,
'anu, vavDaj, 'antam, SoSDaj je ghoS
QeH 'ej SaQ
jatlh,
<vav,
mutIchtaH ghIlghameS
ta' qab vIta'law'bogh DeI!>

'IStar joHvaD jatlh 'anu,
<qay' nuq?
ghIlghameS voDleH DanuQ, qar'a'?
vaj ta'meyqoqlIj qab maq>

vavDajvaD, 'anu, jatlh 'IStar,
<vav,

Tammuz,

your first love.

A small bird,

you hit him and broke his wing.

Now he stands in the forest and cries.

The mighty lion,

but you dug a pit.

He fell in the grave.

The stallion,

honored with battle.

Now a rope strikes him and he drinks dirty water.

The shepherd,

you turned him into a fierce animal.

Thus other shepherds chase him to kill him.

Ishullanu, your father's farmer,

Every day he brought fruit for you.

You turned him into a lizard.

And now me!

What will happen to me?"

When Ishtar heard this,

she went to Anu, her father, and to Antum, her mother.

She was angry and cried.

She said,

"Father,

Gilgamesh keeps insulting me.

He tells of bad deeds that he says I have done!"

Anu said to Princess Ishtar,

"What is the problem?

Were you not annoying King Gilgamesh?

Thus he proclaims your so-called bad deeds."

Ishtar said to her father, Anu,

"Father,

ghIlghameS HoHmeH   QI'tu' tangqa' HInob
QI'tu' tangqa' Danobbe'chugh,
ghe''or lojmIt vIpummoH
'ej Sal HeghwI' 'e' vIchaw'
'ej yInwI' Sop!
HeghwI' law' law' yInwI' law' puS!>

'IStar joHvaD jatlh 'anu,
<QI'tu' tangqa' vInob 'e' DapoQchugh,
qaStaHvIS Soch DIS 'uruqvaD Soj lIngbe' yotlh
nuvvaD tIr DaboS'a'?
Ha'DIbaHvaD Soj tu'lu''a'?>

vavDajvaD, 'anu, jatlh 'IStar,
<HISlaH, vav
qaStaHvIS Soch DIS   chImtaHvIS yotlh,
nuvvaD tIr vIboSta'
'ej Ha'DIbaHvaD Soj tu'lu'>

mu'Daj QoyDI' 'anu,
ghopDajDaq QI'tu' tangqa' tlhegh lan
ghorDaq QI'tu' tangqa' Dev 'IStar
'uruq lughoS
mol tIn poSmoH QI'tu' tangqa' bey,
'ej molDaq pum wa'vatlh 'uruq loD Qup
mol tIn poSmoH beyDaj cha'DIch,
'ej molDaq pum cha'vatlh 'uruq loD Qup
mol tIn poSmoH beyDaj wejDIch,
molDaq pum 'enqIyDu   'ach pumchu'be'
Sup 'enqIyDu,
'ej QI'tu' tangqa' DuQwI' 'uch 'enqIyDu
tlhopDaq tlhIS tangqa'
veQ jaD tlhuQDaj
nogh tangqa' 'ej 'om
tangqa' tlha' 'enqIyDu

give me the Bull of Heaven so he can kill Gilgamesh.
If you do not give the Bull of Heaven,
I will cause the Gates of Hell to fall.
And let the dead ascend.
And they will eat the living!
The dead outnumber the living!"

Anu said to Princess Ishtar,
"If you demand that I give the Bull of Heaven,
for seven years the fields will not provide food for Uruk.
Did you collect grain for the people?
Is there food for the animals?"

Ishtar said to her father, Anu,
"Yes, father.
While the fields are empty for seven years,
I will have collected grain for the people.
And there will be food for the animals."

When Anu heard her words,
he placed the rope to the Bull of Heaven in her hand.
Ishtar led the Bull of Heaven to the surface.
They went to Uruk.
The snort of the Bull of Heaven opened a large pit,
and one hundred young men of Uruk fell into the pit.
His second snort opened a large pit,
and two hundred young men of Uruk fell into the pit.
His third snort opened a large pit,
Enkidu fell into the pit but he did not fall all the way in.
Enkidu jumped out,
and Enkidu held on to the horns of the Bull of Heaven.
The Bull spit in front of him.
His tail flung trash about.
The Bull writhed and resisted.
Enkidu chased the Bull.

tangqa' wam 'enqIyDu
tlhuQ 'uch
cha' ghop lo' 'ej 'uchchu'
QI'tu' tangqa' ghoS ghIlghameS jaq
yanDaj lo' ghIlghameS 'ej jop
tangqa' mong jeq ghIlghameS yan

QI'tu' tangqa' luHoHta'DI',
tlq lulel 'ej SamaSvaD lumuch

'uruq yerghoDaq Qam 'IStar
'IQ 'ej QeH 'ej mu'qaD bach
jatlh,
<'oy'taHjaj ghIlghameS,
tIchwI',
QI'tu' tangqa' HoHwI'!>

'IStar mu'qaD QoyDI' 'enqIyDu,
tangqa' 'uS teq 'ej qabDaj chuH
jatlh,
<qaSIchlaHchugh Qu' rap vIta' 'ej qaQaw'!>

ghom bel be'pu'   parmaq be'pu' je,
'e' tlhob 'IStar
tangqa' HoHlu'mo' 'IQqu'
tangqa' luquvmoH be'

'uruq loDpu'vaD jatlh ghIlghameS,
<'Iv yoH law' Hoch yoH puS?
'Iv jaq law' Hoch jaq puS?
ghIlghameS yoH law' Hoch yoH puS!
ghIlghameS jaq law' Hoch jaq puS!>

lop 'uruq loD

ram Qong
QongtaHvIS naj 'enqIyDu
vem 'ej jupDajvaD wanI' leghbogh Del

Enkidu hunted the Bull.
He grabbed the tail.
He used both hands and securely held on.
Bold Gilgamesh approached the Bull of Heaven.
Gilgamesh used his sword and lunged.
Gilgamesh's sword protruded from the Bull's neck.

When they had killed the Bull of Heaven,
They took out the heart and presented it to Shamash.

Ishtar stood on the wall of Uruk.
She was sad and angry and hurled curses.
She said,
"May Gilgamesh always be in pain.
Slanderer,
killer of the Bull of Heaven!"

When Enkidu heard the cursing from Ishtar,
he wrenched off the Bull's leg and threw it at her face.
He said,
"If I could reach you I would do the same and destroy you!"

The women of pleasure and the women of love gathered together,
Ishtar requested it.
They mourned because the Bull was killed.
The women honored the Bull.

Gilgamesh said to the men of Uruk,
"Who is the bravest of all?
Who is the boldest of all?
Gilgamesh is the bravest!
Gilgamesh is the boldest!"

The men of Uruk celebrated.

Night came and they slept.
Enkidu had a dream.
He awoke and described his dream to his friend.

nagh beQ Soch

ghIlghameSvaD jatlh 'enqIyDu,
<jupwI',
qatlh ja'chuq Qunpu'?
ghom 'anu 'enlII SamaS je
'enlIlvaD jatlh 'anu,
[QI'tu' tangqa' Humbaba je HoHmo',
HeghnIS wa'!]

jatlh 'enlII,
[Hegh 'enqIyDu 'e' chaw'lu'
'ach Heghbe'nIS ghIlghameS!]

'ach 'enlIlvaD jang SamaS
jatlh,
[QI'tu' tangqa' Humbaba je HoHmeH vIra'
DaH HeghnIS'a' 'enqIyDu chun?]

SamaSmo' QeHchoH 'enlII
jatlh,
[Hoch jaj lengtaHvIS Datlhejmo', jup rur!]>

ghIlghameS tlhopDaq Qot 'enqIyDu, rop
SaQ ghIlghameS
jatlh,
<loDnI', loDnI'oy, qatlh?>

jatlh 'enqIyDu,
<vaj DaH qa' vImojnIS'a'?
HeghwI' qa'pu' vItlhej
not loDnI'wI' quv vIleghqa'>

'enlIlvaD jatlh 'enqIyDu,
<SIyDIr vIpe'be'
SIyDIr ngemDaq Humbaba vIHoHbe'>

Tablet VII

Enkidu said to Gilgamesh,
"My friend,
why are the gods conversing?
Anu, Enlil and Shamash are meeting.
Anu said to Enlil,
'Because they killed the Bull of Heaven and Humbaba,
one must die!'

Enlil said,
'Let Enkidu die,
but Gilgamesh must not die!'

But Shamash answered to Enlil,
saying,
'I commanded them to kill the Bull of Heaven and Humbaba.
Now, must innocent Enkidu die?'

Enlil became angry at Shamash
He said,
'Because you traveled with them every day, like a friend!'"

Enkidu was lying in front of Gilgamesh, sick.
Gilgamesh cried.
He said,
"Brother, dear brother, why?"

Enkidu said,
"So now must I become a spirit?
I will accompany the spirits of the dead.
I will never again see my honored brother."

Enkidu said to Enlil,
"I did not cut the Cedar.
I did not kill Humbaba in the Cedar Forest."

mInDu'Daj pep 'enqIyDu
lojmItvaD jatlh,
<Sor Hap lojmIt QIp!
bIyajlaHbe'
SoHvaD Sor vIwIv
nIv Sor
nI'pIrDaq qaqeng
tlho'lIj 'oH wanI'vam'e' 'e' vISovchugh,
'obmaQwIj vIwoH 'ej qape' 'ej qaQaw'!>

'enqIyDu Qoy ghIlghameS 'ej SaQ
'enqIyDuvaD jatlh ghIlghameS,
<jup,
qatlh mu'vetlh Dajatlh?
Qunpu' vIghoS 'ej jIqoy'
'enlII vIghoS 'ej jIqoy'
Dururbogh Hew vIchenmoH>

jajlo' nachDaj pep 'enqIyDu 'ej SamaSvaD jach
jatlh,
<jIqoy', SamaS Dun, jIyInmeH jIqoy'!
vonwI'vetlh
je''eghmeH Soj yap Suqbe'jaj vonwI'
HuchDaj Hoch natlhjaj>

vonwI' 'IghmoHta'DI',
parmaq be' qel tIqDaj
bel be' 'IghmoH
jatlh,
<parmaq be',
yatlhchoHbe'jaj
not puq Daghajjaj!
qorDu' Daghajbe'jaj
mopIIj lammoHjaj chechwI'

Enkidu raised his eyes.
He spoke to the door,
"Stupid wooden door!
You are not able to understand.
I chose the tree for you.
The tree was superior.
I carried you to Nippur.
If I had known that this would be your gratitude,
I would have picked up my ax and chopped you
and destroyed you!"

Gilgamesh listened to Enkidu and cried.
Gilgamesh said to Enkidu,
"Friend,
why do you speak those words?
I will go to the gods and I will beg.
I will go to Enlil and beg.
I will make a statue of you."

At dawn Enkidu raised his head and shouted to Shamash,
saying,
"I beg, Great Shamash, I beg for my life!
That trapper.
May the trapper not acquire enough food to feed himself.
May he use up all of his money."

When he had cursed the trapper,
his heart turned to the harlot.
He cursed the harlot,
saying,
"Harlot,
May you not become pregnant.
May you never have a child!
May you not have a family.
May a drunk soil your robe.

juH DaDabbe'jaj
qevpoblljDaq nIqIpjaj chechwI' chechHa'wI' je
nIjjaj bebllj>

'enqIyDu mu' QoyDI' SamaS,
pay' chalvo' maq
jatlh,
<'enqIyDu,
qatlh Sam'at Da'IghmoH?
SoHvaD Soj HIq je nob
DatuQmeH   Sut le' nob
ghIlghameS, jupII', lIH
DaH loDnI'lI' ghaH ghIlghameS'e'!
bIHeghpu'DI',
lamchoH jIbDaj 'ej targh DIr tuQ,
'ej Hatlh chIm leng>

SamaS mu' QoyDI' 'enqIyDu,
jotchoH tIqDaj
QeHbe'choH
be'vaD jatlh 'enqIyDu,
<Sam'at,
DaH DunaD Du'IghmoHta'bogh nujwIj!
nItlhejjaj qumwI'pu' joHpu' je
Du'ombe'jaj mang, SoHvaD ngaQHa' qoghDaj
SoHvaD Separ baSmey le' je nobjaj
SoHmo' be'nal, SoS, lonlu'jaj>

nogh 'enqIyDu qoD
QottaHvIS mob
jupDajvaD Hoch 'ang
jatlh,
<HIQoy jupwI'
wa'Hu' ram jInaj
jach chal 'ej jang yav

May you not dwell in a home.
May the drunk and the sober strike you on your cheek.
May your roof leak."

When Shamash heard the words of Enkidu,
he suddenly proclaimed from the sky,
saying,
"Enkidu,
why do you curse Shamhat?
She gave you food and wine.
She gave you special clothes to wear.
She introduced Gilgamesh, your friend.
Now Gilgamesh is your brother!
After you die,
his hair will become dirty and he will wear boar skins,
and he will roam the wilderness."

When Enkidu heard the words of Shamash,
his heart became calm.
He was no longer angry.
Enkidu spoke to the women,
"Shamhat,
Now my mouth, which had cursed you, praises you!
May lords and governors accompany you.
May the soldier not resist you, his belt unlocked for you.
May he give you sapphire and exceptional metals.
May the wife, a mother, be abandoned because you."

Enkidu's inside churned.
He was alone lying there.
He revealed everything to his friend.
He said,
"Hear me, my friend.
Last night I had a dream.
The sky cried out and the ground replied.

jojDaq jIQam

nargh loD

'anju rur qabDaj

vIghro''a' namwech rur ghopDaj

toQ pach rur nItlhpachDaj

jIbwIj 'uch 'ej muSev

jIjop 'ach nomqu' vIH

muqIp 'ej mutaHmoH, jIyoy

porghwIj naQ Dech 'ej mutap

jIjach

jIjatlh,

[HIQaH jupwI'!]

'ach chotoDbe'

bIghoSvIp

tel moj DeSDu'wIj, toQ rur

mu'uch, muDev

HurghtaHghach juH,

Daq'e' Dabbogh 'Irqalla,

juH'e' 'ellu'bogh 'ach mejbe'lu'bogh,

wovbe'bogh juH,

Soj 'oH lam'e',

Hurgh,

pa' wIghoS

voDleH mIv'a'mey lughommoHlu'ta', HuD rur

Dat HuDmeyvam lutu'lu'

puH che'ta'bogh mIv'a' tuQwI'pu' vIQoy

DaH 'anuvaD 'enIIlvaD je Ha'DIbaH lujab

bIQ bIr luqang

juHDaq ba' lalDan DevwI'

pa' ba' 'etana

pa' ba' Sumuqan

pa' ba' 'ereSqI'ghal, ghe''or joH

be' tlhopDaq tor bel'etSIrrIy, ghe''or qonwI'

HeghwI' San tetlh 'uch

'ereSqI'ghalvaD laDtaH

I stood between.

A man appeared.

His face resembled Anzu.

His hands like a lion's paws.

His nails were like an eagle's claws.

He seized my hair and contained me.

I lunged but he was too quick.

He hit me and flipped me around, I was upside down.

He surrounded my entire body and squashed me.

I cried out.

I said,

'Help me, my friend!'

But you did not save me.

You were afraid to come.

My arms became wings, like a bird.

He held me, he led me.

The House of Darkness,

the dwelling of Irkalla,

the House that one enters but does not leave,

the House which has no light,

dirt is food,

dark,

we went there.

Kings' crowns were piled up like mountains.

These mountains were everywhere.

I heard the wearers of the crowns which had once ruled the land.

Now they serve meat to Anu and Enlil.

They pour cold water.

In the House sat the priests.

There sat Etana.

There sat Sumukan.

There sat Ereshkigal, Queen of the Netherworld.

Beletseri, Scribe of the Netherworld, knelt before the women.

She held the list of the fates of the dead.

She was reading it to Ereshkigal.

nachDaj pep 'ej muleghDI' jatlh,
[loDvam tlhapta' 'Iv?]>

jatlh ghIlghameS,
<najpu' jupwI'
maQmIgh 'oH wanI'vam'e'>

jaj wa'DIch QongDaqDajDaq Qot 'enqIyDu
jaj cha'DIch QottaH
jaj wejDIch jaj loSDIch je QottaH
vaghDIch javDIch SochDIch je QottaH
chorghDIch HutDIch wa'maHDIch je QottaH
ropqu'choH
wa'maH wa'DIch wa'maH cha'DIch je ropqu'choHtaH

QongDaqDajDaq ba' 'enqIyDu
ghIlghameSvaD jatlh 'enqIyDu,
<vI'IghmoHlu', jupwI'
jI'Ighqu'
che'ronDaq jISuvtaHvIS jIHeghbe'
jIQojvIppu' vaj not jIroj
Do' SuvtaHvIS Heghbogh nuv
batlhHa' jIHegh>

Qotqa' 'enqIyDu
QongchoH
DopDajDaq ba' ghIlghameS

She raised her head and when she saw me said,
'Who has taken this man?'"

Gilgamesh said,
"My friend has had a dream.
This dream is an evil omen."

First day, Enkidu lies in his bed.
A second day, he lies.
A third day and a fourth day, he lies.
A fifth, sixth, and seventh, he lies.
An eighth, ninth, and tenth, he lies.
He became very sick.
An eleventh and twelfth, he grew more sick.

Enkidu sat up in his bed.
Enkidu said to Gilgamesh,
"I have been cursed, my friend.
I am really cursed.
I do not die fighting on the battlefield.
I was afraid to battle, so I will never be at peace.
A person that dies while fighting is fortunate.
I die dishonorably."

Enkidu lied back down.
He fell asleep.
Gilgamesh sat at his side.

nagh beQ chorgh

jajlo' jupDajvaD jatlh ghIlghameS,
<'enqIyDu,
bIboghDI' nItlhej Ha'DIbaH
nImchaj DatlhutlH
tIr tlhol DaSop
Heghtay lulopjaj Hoch
SoHmo' 'IQjaj 'uruq quppu'
SoHmo' 'IQjaj HuD loD
'IQjaj yotlh 'ej jachqu'jaj, SoSII' lurur
'IQjaj SIyDIr DIQaw'bogh
SoHmo' 'IQjaj Hoch Hatlh Ha'DIbaH
SoHmo' 'IQjaj 'ulaj'a bIQtIq quv
SoHmo' 'IQjaj yu'reytIy watlh
SoHmo' 'IQjaj 'uruq loDpu'
SoHmo' 'IQjaj wIjwI'
SoHmo' 'IQjaj parmaq be', bel be'
'IQjaj loDnI'pu', be'nI'pu' rur
SoHmo' jI'IQ

HIQoy 'uruq qup!
HIQoy loD!
jupwI'mo', 'enqIyDu, Heghtay vIlop
jupwI'mo', 'enqIyDu, jI'IQqu'
SoH, jIH DopDaq 'obmaQ'e' tu'lu'bogh, qavoqlaH,
SoH, jIH DopDaq yan'e' tu'lu'bogh,
jIH tlhopDaq yoD'e' tu'lu'bogh,
SoH, SutwIj le',
Ha'quj
nargh qa' mIgh 'ej jIHvo' ghaH nge'!
'enqIyDu, jupwI',
mamuvchuq 'ej HuD wIghoS
QI'tu' tangqa' wISuv 'ej wIHoH
SIyDIr ngem Dabbogh Humbaba'e' wIchargh

Tablet VIII

At dawn Gilgamesh said to his friend,
"Enkidu,
when you were born the animals accompanied you.
You drank their milk.
You ate the raw grain.
May everyone observe the death ritual.
May the elders of Uruk mourn you.
May the men of the mountains mourn you.
May the fields mourn and cry out, as if they were your mother.
May the cedar which we destroyed mourn.
May all the animals of the wilderness mourn you.
May the honored River Ulaja mourn you.
May the pure Euphrates mourn you.
May the men of Uruk mourn you.
May the farmer mourn you.
May the women of love and the women of pleasure mourn you.
May brothers mourn, like sisters.
I mourn you.

Hear me, elders of Uruk!
Hear me, men!
Because of my friend, Enkidu, I perform the death ritual.
Because of my friend, Enkidu, I am very sad.
You, ax at my side, I can trust you,
you, sword at my side,
shield in front of me,
you, my special cloths,
sash;
an evil spirit appeared and took him away from me!
Enkidu, my friend,
we joined together and we went to the mountains.
We fought the Bull of Heaven and we killed it.
We conquered Humbaba who lived in the Cedar Forest.

DaH DuQongqu'moH nuq?
bIHurghchoH 'ej choQoybe'!>

vIHbe' 'enqIyDu mInDu'
tIqDaj Hot, 'ach vIHbe'choHpu'
jupDaj qab So', naywI' rur

jajlo' 'uruq loD ghoS ghIlghameS
jatlh ghIlghameS,
<SoH, baS po'wI',
SoH, Dochmey chenmoHwI',
SoH, Hew chenmoHwI'
jupwI' yIchenmoH,
'enqIyDu rurbogh Hew yIchenmoH>

qaStaHvIS jav pem   Soch ram je,
Heghmo' jupDaj 'IQ ghIlghameS
'IQ 'uruq nuv
'IQchoH nuv Quch

jIbDaj chIp ghIlghameS
SutDaj le', voDleH Sut, teq 'ej woD

lamchoH jIbDaj
veDDIr tuQ 'ej HatlhDaq leng

Now what has put you into this deep sleep?
You become dark and you do not hear me!"

Enkidu's eyes did not move.
He touched his heart, but there was no beat.
He covered his friend's face, like a bride.

At dawn, Gilgamesh went to the men of Uruk.
Gilgamesh said,
"You, metal expert,
you, maker of things,
you, sculptor,
make my friend,
make a statue that is like Enkidu."

For six days and seven nights,
Gilgamesh mourned for his friend.
The people of Uruk mourned.
Happy people became sad.

Gilgamesh clipped his hair.
He removed his special clothing, the clothing of a king,
and threw them away.
His hair became dirty.
He wore animal skins and roamed the wilderness.

nagh beQ Hut

HatlhDaq lengtaHvIS,
jupDajmo', 'enqIyDu, SaQqu' ghIlghameS
jatlh,
<jIHegh'a'?!
marap 'enqIyDu jIH je, qar'a'?!
'IQqu'taH qa'wI'
jIHeghvIp, vaj DaH HatlhDaq jIleng
'ubartu'tu puqloD, 'utanapIStIm Sep vIghoS
nom jIghoS!
HuDDaq jIpawDI' vIghro"a'mey vIlegh
mughIj!
nachwIj vIpep 'ej SInvaD jItlhobneS
jIjatlh,
[HItoD!
Dochvetlh mIgh tInge'!]>

ma'Su HuD
Sal Hov'a' 'ej ghIr Hov'a',
Hoch jaj 'e' 'av HuDvam
HuDvam DungDaq chal neH tu'lu'
bIngDaq ghe"or neH tu'lu'

ma'Su HuD pawDI' lojmIt lu'av Dep
luleghlu'DI' Hegh leghlu'
HoSghaj qa'chaj
ghIlghameS lughIj
'ach SeH'egh ghIlghameS 'ej chol

be'DajvaD jatlh Dep,
<nughoSbogh ghaH, Qun ghaH!>

jang Dep be',
jatlh,

Tablet IX

While roaming the wilderness,
Gilgamesh cried because of his friend, Enkidu.
He said,
"Am I going to die?!
Am I not like Enkidu?!
My soul is very sad.
I am afraid to die, so now I roam the wilderness.
I will go to the region of Utanapishtim, son of Ubartutu.
I will go quickly!
When I arrived at the mountains I saw lions.
I was afraid!
I raised my head and prayed to Sin.
I said,
'Save me!
Take those evil things away!'"

Mount Mashu.
Every day this mountain guards
the rising and setting of the sun.
Above this mountain, only sky.
Below, only hell.

When he arrived at Mount Mashu, beings were guarding the gate.
When one looked upon them, one saw death.
Their spirits were powerful.
Gilgamesh feared them.
But Gilgamesh controlled himself and drew near.

The being said to his female,
"He which comes to us, he is a god!"

The female being answered,
she said,

92

<jub javmaH jav vatlhvI' ghaH, Qun rur,
jubbe' wejmaH wej vatlhvI' ghaH, Human rur>

jach Dep loD
Qunpu' puqvaD jatlh,
<qatlh chuq tIqqu'Daq bIlengta'?
qatlh naDev DaghoS?
ngoQlIj HIja'
Qu'lIj yIQlj
vIghro"a' DIr DatuQ
lamqu' jIblIj
leng nI' DaSIQlaw'>

jatlh ghIlghameS,
<qempa'wI'mo', 'utanapIStlm, jIghoS,
Qun yej muvbogh 'utanapIStlm,
'ej ghaH jubchoHmoHlu'bogh
Hegh yIn je wIqelnIS
Hegh ngoD yIn ngoD je vIghojnIS!>

ghIlghameSvaD jatlh Dep,
<not loD tu'lu', ghIlghameS,
ta'laHta'bogh loD'e'
HuD charghta' pagh
Hurghqu'chu' wejmaH qelI'qam 'abbogh He
wovbe'chu'qu'
leghbe'lu'>

jatlh ghIlghameS,
<jI'IQtaHvIS,
jI'oy'taHvIS,
jIbIrtaHvIS pagh jItujtaHvIS,
jItaH!
DaH lojmIt yIpoSmoH!>

ghIlghameSvaD jatlh Dep,
<yIruch ghIlghameS!

"He is two-thirds god,
one-third human."

The male being called out.
He said to the offspring of the gods,
"Why have you traveled such a long distance?
Why do you come here?
Tell me your purpose.
Explain your quest.
You wear the skin of a lion.
Your hair is filthy.
You apparently endured a long journey."

Gilgamesh said,
"I come because of my ancestor Utanapishtim,
Utanapishtim who joined the Assembly of the Gods,
and was given eternal life.
We must consider death and life.
I must learn the facts of death and life!"

The being said to Gilgamesh,
"There has never been a man, Gilgamesh,
a man who could do that.
None have conquered the mountain.
complete darkness for twelve leagues.
A complete lack of light.
One does not see."

Gilgamesh said,
"While I am sad,
while I am in pain,
while I am cold or hot,
I will go on!
Now open the gate!"

The being said to Gilgamesh,
"Proceed Gilgamesh!

SoHvaD ma'Su HuD vInob
bISIQjaj
poS HuD lojmIt>

'e' QoyDI' ghIlghameS lengchoH

wej qell'qam leng
Hurghqu', wovbe'chu'
'et 'o' joq leghlaHbe'

jav qell'qam leng
Hurghqu', wovbe'chu'
'et 'o' joq leghlaHbe'

Hut qell'qam leng
Hurghqu', wovbe'chu'
'et 'o' joq leghlaHbe'

wa'maH cha' qell'qam leng
Hurghqu', wovbe'chu'
'et 'o' joq leghlaHbe'

wa'maH vagh qell'qam leng
Hurghqu', wovbe'chu'
'et 'o' joq leghlaHbe'

wa'maH chorgh qell'qam leng
Hurghqu', wovbe'chu'
'et 'o' joq leghlaHbe'

cha'maH wa' qell'qam leng
Hurghqu', wovbe'chu'
'et 'o' joq leghlaHbe'

cha'maH loS qell'qam leng 'ej jach
Hurghqu', wovbe'chu'
'et 'o' joq leghlaHbe'

I give the Mashu mountains to you.
May you endure.
The gate of the mountain is open."

When Gilgamesh heard this he began his journey.

One league he traveled.
All was dark, a total lack of light.
He could not see before him nor behind.

Two leagues he traveled.
All was dark, a total lack of light.
He could not see before him nor behind.

Three leagues he traveled.
All was dark, a total lack of light.
He could not see before him nor behind.

Four leagues he traveled.
All was dark, a total lack of light.
He could not see before him nor behind.

Five leagues he traveled.
All was dark, a total lack of light.
He could not see before him nor behind.

Six leagues he traveled.
All was dark, a total lack of light.
He could not see before him nor behind.

Seven leagues he traveled.
All was dark, a total lack of light.
He could not see before him nor behind.

Eight leagues he traveled and cried out.
All was dark, a total lack of light.
He could not see before him nor behind.

cha'maH Soch qell'qam leng
qabDaj roS SuS
Hurghqu', wovbe'chu'
'et 'o' joq leghlaHbe'

wejmaH qell'qam leng 'ej wovchoH

tlhopDajDaq naghbochmey Sormey lutu'lu'
Sor naH bIH Separ'e'
tI bIH Separ'e'
QI'tu' rur Daqvam
'IHqu'
naghboch Doq lutu'lu'
naghboch SuD lutu'lu', bIQ'a' rur
leghqu' ghIlghameS
nuD

Nine leagues he traveled.
The wind licked his face.
All was dark, a total lack of light.
He could not see before him nor behind.

Ten leagues he traveled and light began to appear.

In front of him there were trees of gemstones.
Sapphire were the trees' fruit.
The foliage was sapphire.
This place resembled paradise.
It was very beautiful.
There were red gems.
There were blue gems, like the sea.
Gilgamesh stared.
He looked closely at them.

nagh beQ wa'maH

bIQ'a' HeH Dab SIDurIy, tach QorghwI'
ghaHvaD 'un 'uchwI' chenmoHlu'ta'
ghaHvaD roghbogh HIq ngaSbogh qegh chenmoHlu'ta'
qabDaj So' ngupHom

leng ghIlghameS
DIr tuQ
lam jIbDaj
chuq tIq lengbogh ghot rur

legh tach QorghwI'
SIv
jatlh,
<chotwI' ghaHbej loDvetlh'e'
nuqDaq ghoS?>

ghIlghameS leghDI' tach QorghwI'   lojmIt ngaQmoH
'ach ghIlghameS teSDu' poSmoH wabDaj
leghmeH woSDaj pep ghIlghameS 'ej vaj be' legh
tach QorghwI'vaD jatlh ghIlghameS,
<tach QorghwI', nuq Dalegh?
qatlh lojmItlIj DangaQmoH?
jI'el 'e' Dachaw'Qo'chugh lojmItlIj vIghor!
qaStaHvIS poH nI' HatlhDaq jIleng>

lojmIt ngaQHa'moHQo' be'

tach QorghwI'vaD jatlh ghIlghameS,
<ghIlghameS jIH!
SIyDIr ngem Dabbogh Humbaba'e' vIQaw'chu'
HuDDaq vIghro''a' vIHoH
chalvo' ghoSbogh tangqa' vISuv 'ej vIHoH>

ghIlghameSvaD jatlh tach QorghwI',
<ghIlghameS SoHchugh,

Tablet X

The tavern-keeper Siduri lived at the seashore.
The pot-stand was made for her.
The fermenting vat was made for her.
A veil covered her face.

Gilgamesh roamed about.
He was wearing a skin.
His hair was dirty.
He looked like someone who had traveled a long distance.

The tavern-keeper saw him.
She wondered.
She said,
"That man is certainly a murderer.
Where is he going?"

When the tavern-keeper saw Gilgamesh she locked the door.
But her noise opened Gilgamesh's ears.
Gilgamesh raised his chin to see and thus saw the woman.
Gilgamesh said to the tavern-keeper,
"Tavern-keeper, what do you see?
Why did you lock your door?
If you do not let me in I will break your door!
I roamed in the wilderness for a long time."

The woman would not unlock the door.

Gilgamesh said to the tavern-keeper,
"I am Gilgamesh!
I destroyed Humbaba who lived in the Cedar Forest.
I killed lions in the mountains.
I fought the Bull that came down from heaven and I killed him."

The tavern-keeper said to Gilgamesh,
"If you are Gilgamesh,

SIyDIr ngem Dabbogh Humbaba Qaw'bogh ghaH,
HuDDaq vIghro''a' HoHbogh ghaH,
chalvo' ghoSbogh tangqa' Suvbogh ghaH, 'ej HoHbogh,
qatlh lang qevpobIIj?
qatlh Hurgh mInDu'IIj?
qatlh jach tIqIIj?
qatlh 'IQqu' qa'II'?
qatlh chuq tIq lengbogh ghot Darur?
qatlh HatlhDaq bIleng?>

be'vaD jatlh ghIlghameS,
<tach QorghwI',
lang qevpobwIj
Hurgh mInDu'wIj
jach tIqwIj
'IQqu' qa'wI'
chuq tIq lengbogh ghot vIrur
HatlhDaq jIleng
qatlh?
jupwI', 'enqIyDu, Ha'DIbaH tlhejbogh ghaH
matay'taHvIS HuD wIghoS
QI'tu' tangqa' wISuv 'ej wIHoH
SIyDIr ngem Dabbogh Humbaba'e' wIQaw'
HuDDaq vIghro''a' wIHoH
'enqIyDu, jupwI', ghaH vISaHbogh,
mutlhejbogh ghaH 'ej Hoch ghu' Qatlh DISIQ,
jey loD San
qaStaHvIS jav pem Soch ram je Heghtay vIlop
jI'IQqu'
ghIchDajvo' pumpa' ghew vImolQo'
mughIj SanDaj
jIHeghvIpchoH
vaj   HatlhDaq jIleng
mu'IQmoH jupwI' San
vaj HatlhDaq He tIqDaq jIleng

who killed Humbaba who lived in the Cedar Forest,
who killed lions in the mountains,
who fought the Bull that came down from heaven and killed him,
why are your cheeks thin?
Why are your eyes dark?
Why does your heart cry out?
Why is your spirit so sad?
Why do you look like someone who traveled a long distance?
Why do you roam in the wilderness?"

Gilgamesh said to the woman,
"Tavern-keeper,
My cheeks are thin.
My eyes are dark.
My heart cries out.
My spirit is very sad.
I look like someone who traveled a long distance.
I roamed in the wilderness.
Why?
My friend, Enkidu, who was with the animals.
While together we went to the mountain.
We fought the Bull of Heaven and we killed it.
We destroyed Humbaba who lived in the Cedar Forest.
We killed lions in the mountains.
Enkidu, my friend, whom I care about,
who accompanied me and we endured every hardship,
the fate of man defeated him.
For six days and seven nights I mourned.
I was very sad.
I refused to bury him until a maggot fell from his nose.
His fate scared me.
I began to fear death.
So I roamed in the wilderness.
The fate of my friend made me sad.
So I roamed long trails through the wilderness.

chay' jItamtaH?
chay' jIjotchoH?
lam moj jupwI' vISaHbogh
marapbe"a'?
jIQotchugh jIHu'be"a'?>

jatlh tach QorghwI',
<ghIlghameS, nuqDaq DaghoS?
yIn Danejbogh DaSambe'
Human chenmoHDI' Qun   HumanvaD Hegh lucher
QunvaD yIn lupol
DaH SoH, ghIlghameS,
buy' chorlIj 'e' yIchaw'!
qaStaHvIS pem ram je yIQuch
Hoch jaj   yIlop
pem ram je   yImI'
SutlIj tISay'moH
nachlIj yISay'moH
SoHDaq bIQ yIllch
puqpu' tISaH
be'nal yI'uch 'ej yIbelmoH
Human Qu'na' 'oH ta'vam'e'>

tach QorghwI'vaD jatlh ghIlghameS,
<toH, DaH, tach QorghwI',
'utanapIStIm lurgh yI'ang
He ngu' nuq?
HIja'!
qItchugh bIQ'a' vISIQ
qItbe'chugh HatlhDaq jIlengtaH>

ghIlghameSvaD jatlh tach QorghwI',
<not He tu'lu'
qaSpu'DI' poH tIQ, bIQ'a' SIQ pagh
bIQ'a' SIQlaH SamaS neH
Qatlh He, Qobqu'

How can I stay silent?
How can I be still?
My friend who I care about has become dirt.
Are we not the same?
If I lie down will I not get up?"

The tavern-keeper said,
"Gilgamesh, where are you going?
You will not find the life you are looking for.
When the gods made humans they established death for humans.
They kept life for the gods.
Now you, Gilgamesh,
let your belly be full!
Be happy day and night.
Every day be in celebration.
Dance day and night.
Make your clothes be clean.
Make your head be clean.
Pour water on yourself.
Care about the children.
Hold a wife and please her.
This is the task of humans."

Gilgamesh said to the tavern-keeper,
"So, now, tavern-keeper,
show me the direction of Utanapishtim.
What identifies the path?
Tell me!
If it is possible, I will endure the sea.
If it is not possible, I will roam in the wilderness."

The tavern-keeper said to Gilgamesh,
"There has never been a path.
Since the ancient days none have endured the sea.
Only Shamash can endure the sea.
The course is difficult, it is very dangerous.

jojDaq Hegh bIQmey lutu'lu'
bIQ'a' DaSIQlaHchugh, ghIlghameS,
Hegh bIQ DapawDI' chay' bIvang?
ghIlghameS,
pa' ghaHtaH 'urSanabIy, 'utanapIStIm DeghwI"e'
lutlhej nagh Dochmey
ngemDaq Soj Suq
yIruch, qablIj yI'ang
qItchugh Dulup
qItbe'chugh bIcheghnIS>

mu'vam QoyDI' ghIlghameS,
'obmaQ pep 'ej taj lel
ghoS, QIb rur

'etlh HoSghaj rur, nagh Dochmey ghor
Qaw'

ngem botlhDaq wab Qoylu'
'obmaQ QoyDI' 'urSanabIy,
ghIlghameS legh 'ej ghaHDaq qet
ghIlghameS mevmoH 'e' nID

jatlh ghIlghameS,
<choQaHnIS!>

ghIlghameSvaD jatlh 'urSanabIy,
<qatlh lang qevpobIIj?
qatlh Hurgh mInDu'IIj?
qatlh jach tIqIIj?
qatlh 'IQqu' qa'II'?
qatlh chuq tIq lengbogh ghot Darur?
qatlh HatlhDaq bIleng?>

'urSanabIyvaD jatlh ghIlghameS,
<'urSanabIy,

In between are the Waters of Death.
If you are able to endure the sea, Gilgamesh,
when you arrive at the Waters of Death, what will you do?
Gilgamesh,
over there is Urshanabi, the ferryman of Utanapishtim.
The stone things are with him.
He is in the woods gathering food.
Go on, reveal your face.
If possible, he will transport you.
If it is not possible, you must turn back."

When Gilgamesh heard these words,
he raised his ax and took out his knife.
He went like the shadow.

Like a powerful sword, he broke the stone things.
He destroyed them.

At the center of the woods the noise was heard.
When Urshanabi heard the ax,
he saw Gilgamesh and ran to him.
He tried to stop Gilgamesh.

Gilgamesh said,
"You must help me."

Urshanabi said to Gilgamesh,
"Why are your cheeks thin?
Why are your eyes dark?
Why does your heart cry out?
Why is your spirit so sad?
Why do you look like someone who has traveled a long distance?
Why do you roam in the wilderness?"

Gilgamesh said to Urshanabi,
"Urshanabi,

lang qevpobwIj

Hurgh mInDu'wIj

jach tIqwIj

'IQqu' qa'wI'

chuq tIq lengbogh ghot vIrur

HatlhDaq jIleng

qatlh?

jupwI', 'enqIyDu, Ha'DIbaH tlhejbogh ghaH

matay'taHvIS HuD wIghoS

QI'tu' tangqa' wISuv 'ej wIHoH

SIyDIr ngem Dabbogh Humbaba'e' wIQaw'

HuDDaq vIghro''a' wIHoH

'enqIyDu, jupwI', ghaH vISaHbogh,

mutlhejbogh ghaH 'ej Hoch ghu' Qatlh DISIQ,

jey loD San

qaStaHvIS jav pem Soch ram je Heghtay vIlop

jI'IQqu'

ghIchDajvo' pumpa' ghew vImolQo'

mughIj SanDaj

jIHeghvIpchoH

vaj HatlhDaq jIleng

mu'IQmoH jupwI' San

vaj HatlhDaq He tIqDaq jIleng

chay' jItamtaH?

chay' jIljotchoH?

lam moj jupwI' vISaHbogh

marapbe''a'?

jIQotchugh jIHu'be''a'?

DaH, 'urSanablY,

'utanapIStIm lurgh yI'ang

He ngu' nuq?

HIja'!

qItchugh bIQ'a'Daq jIghoS

qItbe'chugh HatlhDaq jIlengtaH!>

my cheeks are thin.

My eyes are dark.

My heart cries out.

My spirit is very sad.

I look like someone who has traveled a long distance.

I roam in the wilderness.

Why?

My friend, Enkidu, who accompanied the animals.

Together we went to the mountain.

We fought the Bull of Heaven and we killed it.

We destroyed Humbaba who lives in the Cedar Forest.

We killed lions in the mountains.

Enkidu, my friend, whom I care about,

who accompanied me and we endured every hardship,

the fate of man defeated him.

For six days and seven nights I mourned.

I was very sad.

I refused to bury him until a maggot fell from his nose.

His fate scared me.

I became afraid of death.

So I roam in the wilderness.

The fate of my friend made me sad.

So I roam the long trails through the wilderness.

How can I stay quiet?

How can I become still?

My friend who I care about has become dirt.

Are we not alike?

If I lie down will I not get up?

Now, Urshanabi,

show me the direction of Utanapishtim.

What identifies the path?

Tell me!

If it is possible, I will cross the sea.

If it is not possible, I will go on roaming in the wilderness!"

ghIlghameSvaD jatlh 'urSanabIy,
<ghopIIjmo', ghIlghameS, bIQ'a'Daq bIlenglaHbe'!
nagh Dochmey DaQaw'ta' 'ej tlheghmey Dateqta'!
ghIlghameS,
'obmaQIIj yItlhap, 'ej ngem yIghoS
wejvatlh naQ tIpe'
chorghmaH 'uj 'abnIS naQ
tIchIp 'ej ret'aqDaq naghHom tIlan
DujHomDaq tIqem>

mu'vam QoyDI' ghIlghameS,
'obmaQDaj woH 'ej tajDaj lel 'ej ngem ghoS
wejvatlh naQ pe'
chorghmaH 'uj 'ab naQ
chIp 'ej ret'aqDaq naghHom lan
DujHomDaq qem

DujHom lutIj ghIlghameS 'urSanabIy je
maghIIlu-DujHom chIj ghIlghameS
vIHchoH
qaStaHvIS wej jaj, jar poQbogh chuq luleng
Hegh bIQmey paw
ghIlghameSvaD jatlh 'urSanabIy,
<yIloS, ghIlghameS
naQ yItlhap
yuvmeH naQ yIlo'
Hegh bIQmey Hotbe'nIS ghopIIj!
cha'DIch yItlhap, ghIlghameS,
wejDIch, naQ loSDIch je
vaghDIch yItlhap, ghIlghameS,
javDIch, naQ SochDIch je
chorghDIch yItlhap, ghIlghameS,
HutDIch, naQ wa'maHDIch je
wa'maH wa'DIch yItlhap, ghIlghameS,

Urshanabi said to Gilgamesh,
"Because of your hand, Gilgamesh, you can not cross the sea!
You have destroyed the stone things and removed the ropes!
Gilgamesh,
take your ax, and go to the forest.
Cut three hundred poles.
The poles must measure sixty cubits in length.
Trim them and place stones on the grips.
Bring them to the boat."

When Gilgamesh heard these words,
he picked up his ax and took out his knife and went to the forest.
He cut three hundred poles.
The poles measured sixty cubits in length.
He trimmed them and placed stones on the grips.
He brought them to the boat.

Gilgamesh and Urshanabi boarded the boat.
Gilgamesh navigated the magillu-boat.
They began to move.
In three days they traveled the distance of a month.
They arrived at the Waters of Death.
Urshanabi said to Gilgamesh,
"Wait, Gilgamesh.
Take a pole.
Use the pole to push.
Your hands must not touch the Waters of Death!
Take a second, Gilgamesh,
a third, and a fourth pole.
Take a fifth, Gilgamesh,
a sixth, and a seventh pole.
Take an eighth, Gilgamesh,
a ninth, and a tenth pole.
Take an eleventh, Gilgamesh,

naQ wa'maH cha'DIch je!>

Hoch naQ natlh ghIlghameS
vaj qoghDaj teq
SutDaj teq
'ej SuS vonmeH DungDaq 'uch

leghtaH 'utanapIStIm
mIS, SIv, jatlh,
<qatlh DujHom nagh Dochmey luQaw'lu'?
'ej qatlh chIjbe' DujHom pIn'a'?
mutoy'be' loDvetlh
lang qevpobDaj
Hurgh mInDu'Daj
jach tIqDaj
'IQqu' qa'Daj
chuq tIq lengbogh ghot rur
HatlhDaq leng>

paw ghIlghameS
DujHom tlhegh bagh
'utanapIStIm legh ghIlghameS 'ej ghoS
jatlh ghIlghameS,
<loD qan, HIQaH>

ghIlghameSvaD jatlh 'utanapIStIm,
<qatlh lang qevpoblIj?
qatlh Hurgh mInDu'lIj?
qatlh jach tIqlIj?
qatlh 'IQqu' qa'lI'?
qatlh chuq tIq lengbogh ghot Darur?
qatlh HatlhDaq bIleng?>

'utanapIStImvaD jatlh ghIlghameS,
<lang qevpobwIj
Hurgh mInDu'wIj

and a twelfth pole!"

Gilgamesh used up every pole.
So he removed his belt.
He took off his clothes,
and he held them above to catch the wind.

Utanapishtim was looking.
He was confused, he wondered, he said,
"Why are the stone things of the boat destroyed?
And why is the boat's master not navigating it?
That man does not serve me.
His cheeks are thin.
His eyes are dark.
His heart cries out.
His spirit is very sad.
He looks like someone that traveled a long distance.
He roams in the wilderness."

Gilgamesh arrived.
He tied the boat's rope.
Gilgamesh saw Utanapishtim and went to him.
Gilgamesh said,
"Old man, help me."

Utanapishtim said to Gilgamesh,
"Why are your cheeks thin?
Why are your eyes dark?
Why does your heart cry out?
Why is your spirit so sad?
Why do you look like someone that traveled a long distance?
Why do you roam in the wilderness?"

Gilgamesh said to Utanapishtim,
"My cheeks are thin.
My eyes are dark.

jach tIqwIj

'IQqu' qa'wI'

chuq tIq lengbogh ghot vIrur

HatlhDaq jIleng

qatlh?

jupwI', 'enqIyDu, Ha'DIbaH tlhejbogh ghaH

matay'taHvIS HuD wIghoS

QI'tu' tangqa' wISuv 'ej wIHoH

SIyDIr ngem Dabbogh Humbaba'e' wIQaw'

HuDDaq vIghro''a' wIHoH

'enqIyDu, jupwI', ghaH vISaHbogh,

mutlhejbogh ghaH 'ej Hoch ghu' Qatlh DISIQ,

jey loD San

qaStaHvIS jav pem Soch ram je Heghtay vIlop

jI'IQqu'

ghIchDajvo' pumpa' ghew vImolQo'

mughIj SanDaj

jIHeghvIpchoH

vaj HatlhDaq jIleng

mu'IQmoH jupwI' San

vaj HatlhDaq He tIqDaq jIleng

chay' jIItamtaH?

chay' jIjotchoH?

lam moj jupwI' vISaHbogh

marapbe''a'?

jIQotchugh jIHu'be''a'?

vaj jIghoSnIS

'utanapIStIm, HopwI' ponglu'bogh, vIqIHnIS

chuq tIqDaq jIleng

HuDDaq jIleng

bIQ'a'Daq jIleng

jIQongbe'

jIDoy' 'ej jIQop

'oy'qu' SomrawwIj

tach vIpawpa' Qopchu' SutwIj

My heart cries out.

My spirit is very sad.

I look like someone that traveled a long distance.

I roam in the wilderness.

Why?

My friend, Enkidu, who was with the animals.

While together we went to the mountain.

We fought the Bull of Heaven and we killed it.

We destroyed Humbaba who lived in the Cedar Forest.

We killed lions in the mountains.

Enkidu, my friend, whom I care about,

who accompanied me and we endured every hardship,

the fate of man defeated him.

For six days and seven nights I mourned.

I was very sad.

I refused to bury him until a maggot fell from his nose.

His fate scared me.

I began to fear death.

So I roamed in the wilderness.

The fate of my friend made me sad.

So I roamed long trails through the wilderness.

How can I stay silent?

How can I be still?

My friend who I care about has become dirt.

Are we not the same?

If I lie down will I not get up?

So I must go.

I must meet Utanapishtim, who is called 'The Faraway.'

I traveled a long distance.

I roamed the mountains.

I crossed the sea.

I did not sleep.

I am tired and I am worn out.

My muscles are very sore.

Before I arrived at the tavern my clothes

targh vIghro''a' Qa' toQ Sargh 'er je vIHoH
Ha'DIbaH vISop 'ej DIrchaj vItuQ
ngaQba' lojmIt!>

ghIlghameSvaD jatlh 'utanapIStIm,
<ghIlghameS,
qatlh bI'IQqang?
javmaH jav vatlhvI' Qun wejmaH wej vatlhvI' Human je SoH
He Dabbogh qoH Daqelta''a'?
qoHvaD SojlIj Danob'a'?
pagh, raghbogh Soj ngo' Danob'a'?
Qop SutDaj
joH mop ghajbe'
Ha'quj tu'be'lu', lam neH tuQ
vuvlu'be'
yISaH, ghIlghameS
Human tu'lu'pa' chut cherlu'ta'
Human San 'oH Hegh'e'
bIvumtaHqu', 'ej nuq Daghaj?
bIQop'eghmoH
bI'IQ'eghmoH
tugh yInlIj DarInmoH
Hegh leghlaH pagh
Hegh qab leghlaH pagh
Hegh ghogh QoylaH pagh
'a yIn nge'bogh Hegh naS'e' tu'lu'
qaStaHvIS DIS 'ar juH wIcher?
qaStaHvIS DIS 'ar mab wIpol?
qaStaHvIS DIS 'ar vavchaj puH lulo' loDnI'pu'?
qaStaHvIS DIS 'ar ghur bIQtIq 'ej yotlh SoD?
not Hov ghor leghlaHbogh qab tu'lu'

chay' rurchuq QongwI' HeghwI' je?
chut maqDI' 'enlIl,

were completely worn out.

I killed boars, lions, and other beasts.

I ate the meat and wore their skin.

The gate is obviously locked!"

Utanapishtim said to Gilgamesh,

"Gilgamesh,

why are you willing to be sad?

You are two-thirds god and one-third man.

Have you considered the fool dwelling in the street?

Did you give your food to the fool?

Or did you give old, decayed food?

His clothes are worn out.

He does not have a robe of a lord.

There is no sash, he wears only dirt.

He is not respected.

Care, Gilgamesh.

Before mankind the law had been established.

Death is the fate of mankind.

You have toiled nonstop, and what do you have?

You have worn yourself out.

You cause yourself to be sad.

Soon you will cause your life to come to an end.

No one can see death.

No one can see the face of death.

No one can hear the voice of death.

But there is a vicious death that takes life away.

For how many years do we establish a home?

For how many years do we keep a treaty?

For how many years do brothers use their father's land?

For how many years has the river increased and flood the field?

There has never been a face that could look upon
the surface of the sun.

How are the sleeping and the dead alike?

When Enlil proclaimed the law,

ghom 'anunnaqIy, Qun'a'pu'
San nab mamme'tam, San cherwI'
Hegh yIn je cher chaH
'a Hegh jajmey Sov pagh>

the Anunnaki, the Great Gods, assembled.
Mammetum, the establisher of fate, planned fate.
They established death and life.
But no one knows the days of death."

nagh beQ wa'maH wa'

'utanapIStImvaD, HopwI', jatlh ghIlghameS,
<qalegh,
'a Hujbe' porghlIj
chorur!
bIpImbe'
chorur!
qaSuv 'e' vIHech
'ach lI'Ha' DeSwIj, qaSuvlaHbe'
HIja',
chay' Qun yejDaq bIQam 'ej yIn DaSam?>

ghIlghameSvaD jatlh 'utanapIStIm,
<Doch So'lu'bogh, ghIlghameS, SoHvaD vI'ang
Qun pegh qaja'!
yu'reytIy HeHDaq Suru'paq tu'lu',
veng DaSovbejbogh
ngo'qu' vengvetlh, 'ej pa' Qunpu' lutu'lu'ta'
SoD'a' qaSmoHmeH   pIlmoH Qun'a'pu' tIq
'Ip maq vavchaj, 'anu
qeSwI'chaj ghaH 'enlII jaq'e'
bIQ lupmeH pIn ghaH 'en'ughIy'e'

tlhej 'Iy'a, joH 'ong,
vaj juHvaD pegh 'ang,
jatlh,
[juH, juH! reD, reD!
HIQoy juH! HIyaj reD!
Suru'paq loD, 'ubartu'tu puqloD
juH yIlagh 'ej Duj yIchenmoH!
mIp yIlon 'ej Depmey tInej!
Doch ram tIwoD 'ej Depmey tIQorgh!
DujDaq Hoch Dep yIn tItIjmoH]

vIyaj

Tablet XI

Gilgamesh said to Utanapishtim, the Faraway,
"I see you,
but your body is not strange.
You are like me!
You are not different.
You are like me!
I intended to fight you.
But my arms are useless, I am unable to fight you.
Tell me,
How did you stand in the Assembly of the Gods and find life?"

Utanapishtim said to Gilgamesh,
"That which is hidden, Gilgamesh, I reveal to you.
I will tell you the secret of the gods!
On the bank of the Euphrates is Shuruppak,
a city that you surely know.
That city is very old, and there were gods there.
The hearts of the Great Gods inspired them to cause the Flood.
Their father, Anu, proclaimed an oath.
Bold Enlil was their adviser.
Ennugi was the Minister of Canals.

Ea, the Clever Prince, accompanied them,
So he revealed the secret to the house,
saying,
'House, house! Wall, wall!
Hear me, house! Understand me, wall!
Man of Shuruppak, son of Ubartutu.
Take apart the house and build a boat!
Abandon wealth and seek beings!
Throw away the unimportant things and take care of the beings!
Make every living being board the boat.'

I understood.

joHwI'vaD, 'Iy'a, jIjatlh,
[joHwI', chora'
qalob 'ej vIta'
'a chay' vengvaD roghvaHvaD qupvaD je jIjang?]

jIH, toywI'Daj, mura' 'Iy'a,
jatlh,
[bIjatlhnIS,
<mulajHa'law' 'enlIl
vaj vengraj vIDablaHbe'
'enlIl yavDaq qam vIlanlaHbe' je
'apSu vIghoS 'ej joHwI', 'Iy'a, vItlhej
'ej tlhIHDaq mIp law' SISmoH ghaH,
Ha'DIbaH law' bIQDep law' je
tlhIHvaD mIp yob ghaH,
po pov je SIS tIr!>]

wewchoHDI' jajlo',
ghom vumwI'pu'
'obmaQDaj qeng Sor po'wI'
luchDaj qeng Duj chenmoHwI' po'
QaH puqpu'
Dochmey qeng je pujwI'pu'

jaj vaghDIch Som vInab 'ej vIchenchoHmoH
tIn, yotlh rur
wa'vatlh javmaH 'uj 'aD reD
rap beb HeHmey,
wa'vatlh javmaH 'uj juch Hoch Dop
qoD vInab 'ej nab vIghItlh
jav tlhoy' SaS tu'lu'
vaj Soch choQ tu'lu'
vIwav, Hut 'ay' tu'lu'
Duj pIpDaq naghmey vIlan
tep pa'Daq vIychorgh qegh law' vIpol
tIr qegh law' vIpol je

I said to my lord, Ea,
'My lord, you command me.
I will obey you and I will do it.
But how shall I answer to the city, the populace, and the elders?'

Ea commanded me, his servant,
he said,
'You must say,
"Enlil has apparently rejected me.
Thus I am not able to dwell in your city.
Nor can I place a foot on Enlil's land.
I will go to the Apsu and accompany my lord, Ea.
And he will cause much wealth to rain down on you.
Numerous animals and abundance of fish.
He will harvest wealth for you.
Morning and afternoon, grain will rain down!'"

When dawn began to glow,
workers gathered.
The expert of trees carried his ax.
The expert ship builder carried his equipment.
Children helped.
The weak also carried things.

On the fifth day I planned the hull and started to construct it.
It was as big as a field.
The walls measured 120 cubits tall.
The sides of the roof were equal,
each side measuring a width of 120 cubits.
I planned the interior and drew out the plans.
There were six levels.
Thus there were seven decks.
I divided them, there were nine sections.
I placed rocks in the ship's spine.
I stored numerous barrels of vegetable oil in the cargo room.
I also stored many barrels of grain.

Hoch jaj SopmeH targh vIHoH
vumwI'vaD HIq vInob
law' HIq, bIQtIq bIQ rur
vaj loplaH, DIS chu' rur
ram Duj luchenmoH 'e' lurIn
Qatlhqu' bIQDaq Duj lanlu'meH Qu'
bIQ 'elpa' bID Duj,
tlhopvo' naQ'a'mey qengnIStaH 'ej 'emDaq lan

naQ'a'meyDaq vIH Duj

DujDaq Hoch vIghajbogh vIlan
DujDaq Hoch baS wagh vIghajbogh vIlan
Duj tIj Hoch yInwI' vIghajbogh
tIj qorDu'wIj
tIj Hoch Dep Ha'DIbaH vumwI'pu'wI' je

poH cher SamaS
jatlh,
[po pov je tIr vISISmoH!
Duj yItIj 'ej lojmIt yISoQmoH 'ej bIQ yIbot!]

paw poHvetlh
po pov je SIS tIr
muD Dotlh vIbej
mughIj muD!
Duj vItIj, lojmIt vISoQmoH 'ej bIQ vIbot
wewchoHDI' jajlo',
chal HeHvo' ghoS 'eng qIj
'eng QommoH 'aDaD
HuDDaq puHDaq je vIH Sullat HanIS je
Duj tlhegh 'uchbogh naQ'e' ghor 'er'aghal
Sech pep 'anunnaqIy,
puH meQmoH qul
'aDaD ta'mo' yay' chal,
'ej wovbogh Hoch HurghchoHmoH

Each day I killed a boar for them to eat.
I gave ale to the workers.
The ale was plentiful, like the river's water,
so they were able to celebrate, as if it were a New Year.
By night they finished the boat.
The task of getting the boat into the water was very difficult.
Before half of the boat was in the water,
they had to keep carrying poles from the front
and place them in back.
The boat moved on the poles.

I placed in the boat all that I had.
I placed in the boat all the silver and gold that I had.
Every living thing I had boarded the boat.
My family boarded.
All the beings, animals, and my workers boarded.

Shamash established the time.
He said,
'Morning and afternoon I will make grain rain down!
Board the boat and close the gate and block the water!'

That time arrived.
Morning and afternoon grain rained down.
I watched the weather.
The weather frightened me!
I boarded the boat, closed the gate and blocked the water.
Dawn began to glow.
A black cloud came from the horizon.
Adad made the cloud rumble.
Shullat and Hanish moved about over the mountains and land.
Erragal broke the poles which held the ropes from the ship.
The Anunnaki raised up the torches,
fire burned the land.
The sky was shocked because of Adad's deeds,
and made all that was light become dark.

puH ghorlu', 'un rur
jaj Hoch vIHqu' SuS'a',
bIQDaq HuD mol
nuvpu' HIv SuS
latlh leghlaH pagh,
SoDDaq ghovchuqlaHbe'
Qunpu' ghIj SoD
HeD, 'anu chalDaq Sal
Qun lughIjmoHlu', yerghoDaq ba'
jach 'IStar, boghtaHvIS puqloDDaj   be' rur
jatlh,
[lam lumoj jaj ngo',
Qun yejDaq mu' mIgh vIlo'mo'!
chay' Qun yejDaq mu' mIgh vIlo'?
nuvpu'wI' Qaw' lot chay' 'e' vIchaw'?!
ben nuvpu'wI' vIchenmoHneS,
'ach DaH bIQ'a' luteb, bIQDep rur!]

'IStar lutlhej 'anunnaqIy Qunpu', 'ej SaQ
nItebHa' ba' 'ej SaQ
meQtaH wuSDu'chaj, 'ojmo'

qaStaHvIS jav pem Soch ram je,
SuS'a' SoD je tu'lu'
jevmo' beQchoH puH
jaj SochDIch jevqu'
noH 'oH SoD'e'

jotchoH bIQ'a'
jevbe'choH
jaj Hoch jIbej
tam Hoch
lam lumojpu' Hoch Humanpu'!
beQ puH, beb rur
yIb vIpoSmoH,
'ej ghIchwIj DopDaq pum yInSIp nIt

The land was broken like a pot.
All day long a great wind moved about,
it buried the mountain in the water.
The wind attacked the people.
No one was able to see another,
they could not recognize each other in the flood.
The Flood frightened the gods.
They retreated, they ascended to the sky of Anu.
The gods were scared, they sat by the city wall.
Ishtar cried out, like a woman giving birth.
She said,
'The old days become dirt,
because I used evil words in the Assembly of the Gods!
How did I use evil words in the Assembly of the Gods?
How did I permit a catastrophe to destroy my people?!
Years ago I so dearly created my people,
but now they fill the sea like fish!'

The gods of the Anunnaki accompanied Ishtar, and they cried.
They sat together and cried.
Their lips burning from thirst.

For six days and seven nights,
there was high winds and flood.
The storm flattened the land.
On the seventh day the storm raged.
The flood was war.

The sea became calm.
The storm stopped.
All day long I watched.
Everything was quiet.
Every human had turned to dirt!
The land was flat like a roof.
I opened a vent,
and fresh air fell upon the side of my nose.

qIvDu'wIjDaq jIpum 'ej SaQ

Dat bIQ tu'lu'
puH vInej
wejmaH qelI'qam 'abbogh chuqDaq nargh Sep

nI'muS HuDDaq Saq Duj
Duj 'uch nI'muS HuD, vIHbe'chu' Duj
wa' jaj cha'DIch je Duj 'uch nI'muS HuD, vIHbe'
jaj wejDIch loSDIch je Duj 'uch nI'muS HuD
jaj vaghDIch javDIch je Duj 'uch nI'muS HuD
jaj SochDIch Dav vIngeH
ghoS Dav 'ach chegh
puH Sambe', SaqlaHbe', vaj jIHDaq chegh
SIwallo vIngeH
ghoS SIwallo 'ach chegh
puH Sambe', SaqlaHbe', vaj jIHDaq chegh
reyvIn vIngeH
ghoS reyvIn 'ej HeD bIQ 'e' legh
Sop, tey, ba' 'ach cheghbe'
vaj Hoch lurghDaq Hoch vIngeH
'ej Qun vIquvmoHmeH targh vIHoH
qul vIchenmoHneS
Soch Soch je bal vIlan
'ej bIngDaq SIyDIr latlh tI je vIlIch
pIw lulargh Qunpu',
'ej targh DungDaq ghom, ghew rur
paw bel'etIllIy
belmoHmeH ghIgh'e' chenmoHbogh 'anu pep
jatlh,
[tlhIH, Qunpu',
mongwIj Dechbogh ghIghvam vIlIjbe',
'ej not jajmeyvam vIlIj je!
tay ghoS Qunpu' net chaw'
'ach tay ghoS 'enlI net chaw'be',
SoD qaSmoHmo' 'ej nuvpu'wI' HeghmoHmo']

I fell to my knees and cried.

There was water everywhere.
I looked for land.
At a distance of twelve leagues a region appeared.

The boat landed on Mt. Nimush.
Mt. Nimush held the boat, the boat was completely still.
One day, and a second, Mt. Nimush held the boat, it did not move.
A third day, and a fourth, Mt. Nimush held the boat.
A fifth day, and a sixth, Mt. Nimush held the boat.
The seventh day I sent a dove.
The dove went, but returned.
It did not find land, it was not able to land, so it returned to me.
I sent a swallow.
The swallow went, but returned.
It did not find land, it was not able to land, so it returned to me.
I sent a raven.
The raven went and it saw the water retreat.
It ate, scraped, sat; but did not return.
So I sent forth all things in every direction.
And to honor the gods I killed a sheep.
I started a fire in offering.
Seven and seven jugs I laid in place.
And underneath I poured cedar and other plants.
The gods smelled the fragrance,
and they gathered over the sheep like flies.
Beletili arrived.
She raised the necklace which Anu made for his pleasure.
She said,
'You, gods,
I will not forget this necklace around my neck,
and I will also never forget these days!
The gods are permitted to come to the ritual.
But Enlil is not permitted to come to the ritual,
because he caused the flood and caused my people to die.'

paw 'enlII
Duj legh 'ej QeHqu'choH
'ayghIyghIy Qunpu'mo' Qay'
jatlh,
[chay' nargh Human?
lotmo' taH pagh Human 'e' vIHech!]

'enlII jaqvaD jatlh nInurta,
[nabvam 'oghlaH 'Iy'a neH!]

'enlII jaqvaD jatlh 'Iy'a,
[SoH, jaqwI',
Qunpu' valwI' SoH
qatlh SoD DaqaSmoH SoH,
'ach qaSchu'bogh wanI' Daqelbe'?
wemlu'DI' wemwI' yIpum
mawlu'DI' mawwI' yIpum
'ach yISaH
yItuv pagh luHoHlu'
SoDbe'chugh, nuv nge'meH nargh vIghro''a'!
SoDbe'chugh, nuv nge'meH nargh targh!
SoDbe'chugh, QaDqu'choH puH 'ej Soj tu'be'lu'!

SoDbe'chugh, puH Qaw'meH nargh 'Irra!
Qun'a'pu' pegh 'angbogh ghaH jIHbe'
'atra'aSIS vInajmoH neH, vaj Qunpu' pegh Qoy

vaj ghaH qelnISlu'!]

Duj 'el 'enlII
ghopwIj 'uch 'ej mughoSmoH
be'nalwI' ghoSmoH je 'ej jIH retlhDaq tormoH
Quchmaj Hot
'ej jojmajDaq QamtaHvIS nuquvmoH
jatlh,
[Human ghaH 'utanapIStIm'e'
'ach DaH,

Enlil arrived.

He saw the boat and became very angry.

He was furious because of the Igigi gods.

He said,

'How did a human escape?

I intended no human to survive the catastrophe!'

Ninurta said to the bold Enlil,

'Only Ea could devise such a plan!'

Ea said to the bold Enlil,

'You, bold one,

you are the Sage of the Gods.

Why did you cause the flood,

but not consider the results?

When one violates, accuse the violator.

When one offends, accuse the offender.

But take care.

Be patient or they will be killed.

If not the Flood, a lion would appear to take away the people!

If not the Flood, a boar would appear to take away the people!

If not the Flood, the land would dry up
and there would be no food!

If not the Flood, Erra would appear to destroy the land!

I am not he which revealed the secret of the Great Gods.

I merely caused Atrahasis to dream,
thus hearing the secret of the gods.

So it is him that must be considered!'

Enlil entered the boat.

He held my hand and made me come.

He made my wife come also and kneel beside me.

He touched our foreheads,

and standing between us, he blessed us.

He said,

'Utanapishtim is human.

But now,

maH, Qunpu' rurchoH 'utanapIStIm be'nalDaj je,
'e' yIchaw'!
Hopbogh bIQtIqmey nuj Dab 'utanapIStIm,
'e' yIchaw']

nutlhap 'ej bIQtIqmey nujDaq maHvaD Daq lucher>

jatlh 'utanapIStIm,
<DaH, SoHmo' Qunpu' ghommoH 'Iv,
yIn Danejbogh DaSammeH?
yIloS!
qaStaHvIS jav pem Soch ram je yIQotQo'>

'ach ba'DI' Doy'choH, vaj QongchoH

be'nalDajvaD jatlh 'utanapIStIm,
<naDev yIlegh!
loD, yIn neHbogh QupwI'!
Qongchu'>

'utanapIStImvaD, HopwI', jatlh be'nalDaj,
<yIHot, yIvemmoH
chegh 'e' yIchaw'
puHDaj ghoS 'e' yIchaw'>

be'nalDajvaD jatlh 'utanapIStIm,
<toj Humanpu' 'ej Dutoj
Ha', ghaHvaD chab yIvut 'ej nachDajDaq yIlan
'ej QottaHvIS ghaH, Hoch jaj tlhoy'Daq yIghItlh>

chabDaj vut 'ej nachDajDaq lan 'ej tlhoy'Daq ghItlh

nonchu' chab wa'DIch
nonchoHII' chab cha'DIch
ragh chab wejDIch
veD rur chab loSDIch

let it be, that
Utanapishtim and his wife shall become like us, the gods!
Let it be, that
Utanapishtim shall dwell far away at the mouth of the rivers.'

They took us and established a place for us
at the mouth of the rivers."

Utanapishtim said,
"Now, who will gather the gods because of you,
so that you will find the life that you are searching for?
Wait!
For six days and seven nights you shall not lie down."

But as soon as he sat down he became tired, thus falling asleep.

Utanapishtim said to his wife,
"See here!
The man, the youth who wanted life!
He has fallen into a deep sleep."

His wife said to Utanapishtim, the Faraway,
"Touch him, wake him.
Let him return.
Let him go back to his land."

Utanapishtim said to his wife,
"Humans deceive and will deceive you.
Come, bake pies for him and place them at his head.
And while he is lying, each day make a mark on the wall."

She baked his pies and placed them
at his head and marked the wall.

The first pie was completely rotten.
The second pie was becoming rotten.
The third pie was decaying.
The forth pie was like fur.

'upchoH chab vaghDIch
jejtaH chab javDIch
chab SochDIch vutlu'
ghaH Hot 'utanapIStIm 'ej vem loD

'utanapIStImvaD jatlh ghIlghameS,
<jIQongbe'
tlhoS jIQongDI' choHot 'ej choghuHmoH!>

ghIlghameSvaD jatlh 'utanapIStIm,
<naDev yIlegh, ghIlghameS
chabIlj tItogh!
tlhoy'Daq ghItlhlu'ta'!
nonchu' chabIlj wa'DIch
nonchoHII' chab cha'DIch
ragh chab wejDIch
veD rur chab loSDIch
'upchoH chab vaghDIch
jejtaH chab javDIch
chab SochDIch vutlu'DI' bIvem!>

'utanapIStImvaD, HopwI', jatlh ghIlghameS,
<va!
chay' jIvangnIS, 'utanapIStIm?
nuqDaq vIghoSnIS?
QongDaqwIj Dab Hegh
Dat SaH Hegh, Dat vIghoSbogh!>

'urSanabIyvaD, DeghwI', jatlh 'utanapIStIm,
<jIHDaq loDvam Daqemta'!
qatlh jIHDaq loDvam Daqemta'?!
Dulonjaj bIQ'a'!
lamqu' loDvam jIb 'ej
DIrDaj 'IH luQIH Ha'DIbaH DIr
ghaH yInge', 'urSanabIy

The fifth pie became unsavory.

The sixth pie was still sharp.

The seventh pie was baked.

Utanapishtim touched him and the man awoke.

Gilgamesh said to Utanapishtim,

"I am not sleeping.

When I almost fell asleep you touched me and alerted me!"

Utanapishtim said to Gilgamesh,

"See here, Gilgamesh.

Count your pies!

The wall is marked!

Your first pie is completely rotted.

The second pie is becoming rotten.

The third pie is decaying.

The forth pie is like fur.

The fifth pie became unsavory.

The sixth pie is still sharp.

When the seventh pie was baked, you awoke!"

Gilgamesh said to Utanapishtim, the Faraway,

"O woe!

What must I do, Utanapishtim?

Where must I go?

Death dwells in my bed.

Death is present everywhere, everywhere I go!"

Utanapishtim said to Urshanabi, the ferryman,

"You brought this man to me!

Why did you bring this man to me?!

May the sea abandon you!

This man's hair is filthy and

The animal skins damaged his beautiful skin.

Take him away, Urshanabi.

Say'moHwI' DaqDaq yIqem
'elu rur, bIQDaq jIbDaj Say'moH 'e' yIchaw'
Ha'DIbaH DIrDaj yIwoD 'ej naDevvo' qeng bIQ'a'

porghDaj Say'moH 'e' yIchaw'
chuQun mop tuQ 'e' yIchaw'!
vengDaj lengpa',
lamchoH chuQun mopDaj 'e' yIchaw'Qo'!
yIchu'moHchu'>

nge' 'urSanabIy
Say'moHwI' DaqDaq qem
bIQDaq jIbDaj Say'moH, 'elu rur
Ha'DIbaH DIrDaj woD 'ej naDevvo' qeng bIQ'a'

porghDaj Say'moH
chuQun mop tuQchoH
vengDaj lengpa',
lamchoHbe' chuQun mopDaj
Say'chu'taH

DujHom lutIj ghIlghameS 'urSanabIy je
maghIllu-DujHom luchIj
vIHchoH

'utanapIStImvaD jatlh be'nalDaj,
<naDev pawDI' ghIlghameS Doy'chu'
batlh puHDaj cheghmeH ghaHvaD nuq DanoblaH?>

vaj   naQ pep ghIlghameS 'ej vergh

ghIlghameSvaD jatlh 'utanapIStIm,
<ghIlghameS, naDev DapawDI' bIDoy'chu'
puHIj DacheghmeH nuq qanobnIS?
Doch So'lu'bogh vI'ang
SoHvaD pegh vI'ang

Bring him to the washing place.
Let him wash his hair in the water, like ellu.
Throw away his animal skins
and the sea will carry them from here.
Let him wash his body.
Let him wear royal robes!
Before he travels to his city,
Do not let his royal robe become dirty!
Make them be perfectly new."

Urshanabi took him away.
He brought him to the washing place.
He cleaned his hair in the water, like ellu.
He threw away his animal skins
and the sea carried them from hear.
He cleaned his body.
He put on a royal robe.
Before he traveled to his city,
his royal robe did not become dirty.
They remained perfectly clean.

Gilgamesh and Urshanabi boarded the boat.
They navigated the magillu-boat.
It began to move.

His wife said to Utanapishtim,
"When Gilgamesh arrived here he was exhausted.
What can you give him so he can return to his land with honor?"

So Gilgamesh raised a pole and docked.

Utanapishtim said to Gilgamesh,
"Gilgamesh, when you arrived here you were exhausted.
What must I give so you can return to your land?
I will reveal a thing that is hidden.
I will reveal a secret for you.

lav tu'lu'
ghoplIj DuQbogh DuQwI'Hom ghaj, neHjej rur
lav SIchchugh ghopDu'lIj loD Qup Damoj>

De'vam QoyDI' 'och poSmoH ghIlghameS
qamDu'DajDaq naghmey 'ugh lan,
'ej 'uchmeH tlhegh bagh
lujotlh, 'apSu ghoS
lav tlhap
ghopDaj 'oy'moH 'a tlhaptaH
qamDu'Dajvo' naghmey teq,
'ej bIQ HeHDaq ghaH vo' bIQ'a' 'e' chaw'

'urSanabIyvaD, DeghwI', jatlh ghIlghameS,
<'urSanabIy,
Doch raghbe'moHbogh lav 'oH lavvam'e'
lavvammo' taHlaH Human
'uruqDaq vIqem
tobmeH lavvam Sop loD qan
[loD Qup moj loD qan] 'oH lavvam pong'e'
vISop 'ej jIQupqa'>

vaghmaH qelI'qam lengta'DI' SopmeH mev
SochmaH vagh qelI'qam lengta'DI' QongmeH mev

ngengHom lutu'
bIr bIQ
ngengHomDaq Say"eghmoH 'ej leS
lav pIw largh ghargh'a'
ghoStaHvIS tam
lav nIH ghargh'a' 'ej nge'
mejtaHvIS   DIrDaj polHa'

ba' ghIlghameS 'ej SaQ
jatlh,
<HIqeS, 'urSanabIy DeghwI'!

There is a shrub.
It has thorns which will prick your hand like a thistle.
If your hands reach the shrub you will become a young man."

When he heard this information, Gilgamesh opened a tunnel.
He placed heavy rocks at his feet,
and tied a rope to hold them.
They took him down, he went to the Apsu.
He took the shrub.
It hurt his hands but he continued to take it.
He removed the rocks from his feet,
and allowed the sea to propel him to the shore.

Gilgamesh said to Urshanabi, the ferryman,
"Urshanabi,
this plant is a plant that makes things not decay.
A human can survive because of this plant.
I will bring it to Uruk.
An old man will eat this shrub to test it.
This shrub's name is 'The Old Man Becomes a Young Man.'
I will eat it and I will be young again."

When they had traveled twenty leagues they stopped to eat.
When they had traveled thirty leagues they stopped to sleep.

There was a pond.
The water was cool.
They wash themselves in the pond and relaxed.
A snake smelled the plant's fragrance.
It came quietly.
The snake stole the shrub and took it away.
While leaving, it shed off it's skin.

Gilgamesh sat and he cried.
He said,
"Counsel me, Urshanabi, the ferryman!

'IvvaD vum DeSDu'wIj, 'urSanabIy?
'IvvaD lamchoH tIqwIj 'Iw?
jIHvaD ta' QaQ vIchavbe'
'ach yav voDleHvaD ta' QaQ vIta'!
DaH vaghmaH qelI'qam 'ab bIQ jen He
'och vIpoSmoHDI' ratlh luchwIj
Daq ngu'meH nuq vISamlaH?
jIchegh 'a bIQ HeHDaq DujHom vIratlhnISmoH!>

vaghmaH qelI'qam lengta'DI' SopmeH mev
SochmaH vagh qelI'qam lengta'DI' QongmeH mev

'uruq lupaw
'urSanabIyvaD, DeghwI', jatlh ghIlghameS,
<yIjaH, 'urSanabIy
'uruq yergho yIghoS 'ej yIyIt
yergho bIng yInuD, yergho naQ yInuDchu'
naghvam nIv law' latlh nagh nIv puS, qar'a'?
nab lucher Soch valchu'wI'
Soch qelI'qam 'IStar chIrgh Daq Huv je,
qat 'uruq yergho>

For whom did my arms toil, Urshanabi?
For whom did the blood of my heart become dirty?
I have not achieved a good deed for myself.
But I accomplished a good deed for the king of the ground!
Now the course of the high water measures twenty leagues.
When I opened the tunnel, my equipment remained.
What can I find to identify the site?
I will return but I must leave the boat at the shore!"

When they had traveled twenty leagues they stopped to eat.
When they had traveled thirty leagues they stopped to sleep.

They arrived at Uruk.
Gilgamesh said to Urshanabi, the ferryman,
"Go, Urshanabi.
Go onto the wall of Uruk and walk.
Inspect under the wall, thoroughly examine the complete wall.
Are not these stones more superior than any other?
The Seven Sages themselves laid out its plan.
Three leagues and the open area of the Ishtar temple,
does the wall of Uruk enclose."

Appendix

Klingon Names

Many of the names attributed to characters and places in this epic are clearly of ancient Terran origin. In the actual Klingon text, the names have undergone an apparent transliteration, mapping them onto the phonological patterns of **tlhIngan Hol**. These renderings, used throughout the translation found on the Gilgamesh Planetoid — and subsequently romanized for the convenience of Federation audiences — are summarized below.

bel'etIllIy - Another name of **'aruru**.

bel'etSIrrIy - A female scribe in the Netherworld.

Dav - A type of bird found on Earth.

ghIlghameS - King of **'uruq**. Son of the goddess **nInSun** and **lughalbanDa**. He is two-thirds god, one-third man.

HanIS - A minor weather god, usually paired with **Sullat**, the two being heralds of the Storm God, **'aDaD**.

Humbaba - Guardian of the **SIyDIr** forest.

lebanan - Coastal region located northwest of **'uruq** and south of Turkey.

lughalbanDa - Father of **ghIlghameS**, husband of **nInSun**.

lullubu - The wild mountain people of western Iran.

maghIllu - Name of a boat. Also appears in another Sumerian myth.

mamme'tam - Another name of the Mother Goddess, **'aruru**.

ma'Su - The mountains through which the sun rises.

nInSun - Mother of **ghIlghameS**.

nInurta - God of war.

nI'muS HuD - The mountain where the boat landed after the Flood.

nI'pIr - The religious city of the god **'enlIl**, located in the center of Mesopotamia.

reyvIn - A type of bird found on Earth.

rIm'at-nInSun - Another name of **nInSun**.

SamaS - The Sun God; god of justice.

Sam'at - The harlot (**parmaq be'**) who seduced **'enqIyDu**.

SIDurIy - The tavern-keeper (**tach QorghwI'**).

SImuru - One of the winds used by **SamaS** against **Humbaba**.

SIn - The Moon God, chief deity of the city Ur, south of **'uruq**.

SIwallo - A type of bird found on Earth.

SIyDIr ngem - The forest which was guarded by the terrible **Humbaba**. Believed to be located in southern Turkey.

SI'par - City of northern Babylonia whose chief deity was **SamaS**.

Sullat - A minor weather god, usually paired with **HanIS**, the two being heralds of the Storm God, **'aDaD**.

Sumuqan - God of wild animals, symbolized by his shaggy skin.

Suru'paq - One of the most ancient cities of Sumer, north of **'uruq**.

tammuj - The god of vegetation. Husband of **'IStar**.

tangqa' - **QI'tu' tangqa'**, the Bull of Heaven. A Klingon animal often described as "bull-like." Both male and female specimens are called **tangqa'**.

yu'reytIy - The western river of the two major rivers of Mesopotamia.

'aDaD - The Storm God.

'aja' - Wife of **SamaS**.

'anju - A mythological lion-headed eagle.

'antam - Mother of **'IStar**.

'anu - The most ancient deity of Sumer, called the Father of the Gods. **'uruq** was his sacred city.

'anunnaqIy - A group of fifty gods, sons of **'anu**. The "Seven Great **'anunnaqIy**" were the seven gods who set the destinies and the only ones who could authorize change in the constitution of the universe.

'apSu - The freshwater sea flowing under the earth, domain of **'Iy'a**.

'aruru - The Mother Goddess. Created mankind.

'atra'aSIS - Epithet applied to **'utanapIStIm**, the survivor of the Flood. The epithet means "exceedingly attentive", or "exceedingly wise."

'ayghIyghIy - A group of gods who were subject to the **'anunnaqIy** and did manual labor for them.

'elu - This name is referenced in Tablet XI, but no information explaining who he is has been found.

'enlIl - God of earth, wind, and spirit. Ultimately in charge of determining destinies. His cult center was in the city **nI'pIr**.

'enqIyDu - Friend of **ghIlghameS**. Created by **'aruru**. Born a primitive man living in the wild among the animals until seduced and domesticated by the harlot **Sam'at**.

'en'ughIy - The Chief Canal Minister of the gods.

'ereSqI'ghal - The "Queen of the Netherworld."

'er'aghal - Husband of 'ereSqI'ghal. With her, ruler of the Netherworld.

'etana - King of the city Kish after the Flood.

'IrnIynIy - Another name of 'IStar, in her ferocious aspect.

'Irqalla - Another name of the Netherworld.

'Irra - God of pestilence.

'IStar - Goddess of love and war, daughter of 'anu.

'IS'ullan'u - A gardener, the last of 'Istar's six lovers in the litany of ruined men in Tablet VI.

'Iyghalma - The temple of nInSun in 'uruq.

'Iy'a - The god of the subterranean freshwater sea 'apSu. Friend of mankind. Often presented as a trickster, using clever stratagems and verbal games to achieve his ends without technically violating the rules.

'Iy'anna - The Temple of 'anu and 'IStar in 'uruq. The name means "House of 'anu."

'ubartu'tu - King of Suru'paq. Father of 'utanapIStIm

'ulaj'a - A river in southwestern Iran.

'urSanabIy - The ferryman (DeghwI') that took ghIlghameS across the "Waters of Death" to 'utanapIStIm.

'uruq - A city of ancient Sumer, located on the Euphrates River in southern Mesopotamia. One of the oldest and most sacred cities of Sumerian history.

'utanapIStIm - The man who was allowed to survive the Flood and was given eternal life. Now lives in a remote corner of the world. He is now sometimes called HopwI', "the Faraway."

Printed in the United Kingdom
by Lightning Source UK Ltd.
93279